IRON STRING

IRON
STRING

Based on a True Story

RUDY REVAK

LEGACY

Iron String
Rudy Revak

Production Editor: Pamela Triolo

FIRST EDITION

HARDCOVER ISBN: 978-1-942545-70-5
PAPERBACK ISBN: 978-1-942545-71-2
eBook ISBN: 978-1-942545-72-9

Library of Congress Control Number: 2016960598

LEGACY

Published by Legacy,
An Imprint of Wyatt-MacKenzie Publishing, Inc.

In memory of my parents
Stefan and Maria Revak.
You always lived your values,
deeply loved each other and your family, and
persevered through every obstacle.
You were my inspiration.

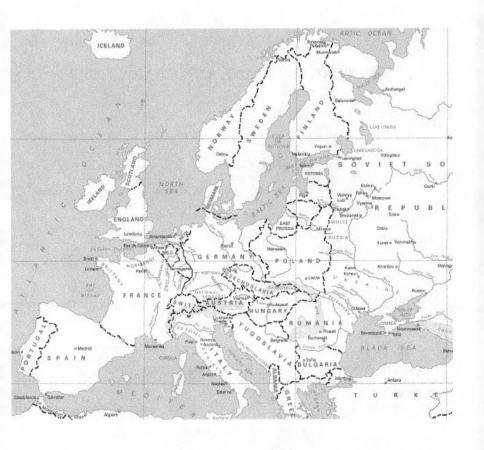

Map of Europe and the Middle East 1943
Courtesy of the United States Military Academy,
Department of History

HISTORIC TIMELINE AND CHARACTERS

September 18, 1889	Stefan Revak born
September 11, 1893	Gertrude Erli born
1910	Gertrude Erli leaves Scheindorf, Romania/Hungary, to work in NYC
January–February 1914	Gertrude Erli returns to marry Stefan Revak
World War I July 28, 1914–Nov. 11, 1918	December 18, 1914, Stefan Revak born (son of Gertrude and Stefan)
1920	Stefan Revak, Sr. leaves Scheindorf for America
January 4, 1921	Maria Ditzig born
February 1925	Stefan Revak, Sr., returns to Scheindorf
May 18, 1936	Stefan Revak (son) conscripted into the Romanian army
November 15, 1937	Stefan Revak (son) marries Maria Ditzig
World War II Sept. 1, 1939–Sept. 2, 1945	March 27, 1942 Stefan Revak (son) conscripted into the Germany army
	October 9, 1944, Evacuation of Scheindorf
	April 30, 1945, Adolf Hitler's suicide
	May 5, 1945, Surrender of Germany
Spring 1951	Stefan, Sr., and Gertrude Revak immigrate to America
April 27, 1952	Stefan (son), Maria, Klothilde, Siglinda, and Rudolf Revak reach America
May 3, 1971	Stefan Revak, Sr., dies
May 24, 1973	Gertrude Revak dies
October 21, 1994	Steven (Stefan) Revak dies
July 3, 2013	Mary (Maria) Revak dies

From left to right: Gertrude Erli Revak; Maria Ditzig Revak
holding Rudolf Revak; Siglinda Revak; Klothilde Revak;
Stefan Revak, Jr.; Stefan Revak, Sr. (1947)

ACKNOWLEDGMENTS

We placed the acknowledgments here because I think it is important for the reader to understand how this book came about. Over twenty-five years ago, I wanted to find a way to save many of the stories we had all heard from my parents and grandparents about their time in Europe, World War II, and their journey to the United States. My intent was to develop a historical book for our family.

We engaged Renee McCarthy to interview and tape my parents, my sisters, and me. From these thirty hours of tapes, Renee wrote the manuscript, "Revak Family History: 1914-1994." I kept it in a box for over twenty years. In fact, I forgot about it. I happened to talk to colleague, Jim Waldsmith about it. Jim took the materials, interviewed my sisters and me, added great military background, many stories of the period, and developed a manuscript he called, "Home is in the Heart." Thank you, Jim, for all you did. You got this idea going again.

Then we moved to the Houston, TX area, and my wife, Pam Allado, and I met some new neighbors, Peter and Pamela Triolo. Pamela was a published writer, and she offered to look at both manuscripts. Peter created electronic files of the tapes. After listening to the tapes and studying the manuscripts, Pamela felt our family history was wonderful, full of lessons of leadership and rich with a love story, and encouraged me to publish a new manuscript. I agreed.

The book you see today is here because of time and talents of many people. I owe special thanks to my sisters,

Linda (Siglinda) Revak Muller, her husband George, my sister, Hilda (Klothilde) Revak Gloss and her husband Don, for their stories as well as their review and critique of the manuscript. Rachel Starr Thomson did a super job of editing and copyediting, suggesting changes that helped us with storytelling, character development, and pace. We thank the alpha and beta readers who gave us impressions and advice along the way: my wife, Pam, Katie Gibbs, Tiana King, and Peter Triolo.

We are grateful for the rapid response of LTC (Ret.) Raymond A Hrinko, United States Military Academy, Department of History, for the use of the maps featured on the cover and in the book's interior. Nancy Cleary, Publisher, Wyatt-MacKenzie Publishing, was an amazing graphic designer for our cover and a responsive and wonderful publishing partner.

So how did we get this finally get to this book version of our family's story? After weeks of talking with Pamela Triolo, she agreed to serve as our ghostwriter and production editor. She took the audiotapes and manuscripts, researched history for facts that added credibility to the story, worked with my wife, my family, and me to write historical scenes that were true to the personalities, hearts, and souls of my parents and grandparents. I even cooked my mom's sausage and potato soup for all of us! Pamela responded to Rachel's feedback and those of the alpha and beta readers, and guided us to the book that you see today.

As I did in the beginning, I want to thank my mom and dad. I hope that this book leaves a bit of a legacy of all you did for us. We think about you every day. You live on in the lives of everyone you touched. As you taught us, perhaps this book will teach others.

> *"Trust thyself:*
> *every heart vibrates to that*
> *iron string."*

Ralph Waldo Emerson, *Self-Reliance*

PROLOGUE

*"The greater the lie, the greater the chance
it will be believed."*
"Great liars are also great magicians."
Adolf Hitler

Somewhere in Slovakia
October 8, 1944

THE INKY DARKNESS of the moonless night and the dense canopy of the forest rendered them blind. The Third Reich *Wehrmacht* trainees stumbled over rocks and roots, losing their balance as they carried their bulky military packs. Unseen branches scratched their faces, and the muddy path through the woods was slippery with leaves. It started to rain, drizzling at first, and then sheets of rain fell mixed with sleet, soaking through their wool uniforms.

Obergefreiter Stefan Revak of the German army followed the single file of twenty young men on their first night training drill. He listened, waiting for the whisper of a warning. The last short week had been spent training them in weaponry and landscape battle strategy. He had tried to teach them how to stay alive—to kill to stay alive, not risk their lives to kill. The youngest of them were zealots, raised from birth to believe in the cause,

1

and they were hungry to serve. The combination of their naïveté and zeal for the thrill of battle would likely get them killed.

The senior lance corporal dreaded what was ahead. He had been through many of these rites of passage, and he hated every single one. He waited, listening. All he heard was the slap of boots in mud and the steady beat of the rain.

Suddenly, gunfire erupted ahead of them, briefly illuminating the darkness. The flash from the machine guns was low to the ground, strafing the forest. *Too low! Too low! The bastards!* It was always the bullies in the company who volunteered for this duty. It gave them a rush to test the new soldiers' endurance and ability to survive under live gunfire. Soldiers with a conscience, many of them fathers, spent the night hunkered down in their bunks, suffering from survivor guilt, knowing there would be casualties.

Initiation into the brotherhood of the military was brutal. How could he protect them?

"Take cover! Take cover! Stay down!" Stefan screamed over the gunfire.

The new soldiers scattered.

Mortar fire lit up the sky, and the shooting stars of death arched up, then down, blasting trees and sending shrapnel flying. Stefan ducked and flinched. The young man immediately ahead of him lost his footing and fell back.

Stefan reached down and pulled him up by his pack. The young soldier's knees buckled. He flopped facedown into the mud.

Stefan pulled him up again.

"Come on, you can do it," Stefan said.

The soldier fell limp.

He did not move.

Stefan got down on one knee and rolled the young man over. He pulled out his flashlight and shined it on the face of the fallen soldier. Sightless blue eyes stared back at him. Sadness hit Stefan like a punch in the chest. He closed the young man's eyes and quickly made the sign of the cross. There was no time for a prayer. He needed to save others. Stefan looked at the pink, smooth round face of the boy and quickly judged him to be about thirteen. A mother had lost a son. He was a father. He understood. Anger welled up in him, mingling with grief. *Damn Hitler! His sick lust for power is killing our children. Germany must be desperate.*

Stefan dragged the boy off the path. He did not even know his name.

———————

Stefan walked swiftly across the compound. He was furious.

Hans Fisher. The young soldier was no longer nameless to him. He would search for the family's location and write a letter of compassion, telling the parents their son had died with honor. Three other new soldiers, all under age fifteen, were wounded. They would recover to become enemy targets the next time.

This war was getting out of control, slaughtering tens of thousands of men. Those being conscripted into the German army now were either young boys or older men. After five years of war, most of the men of appropriate military age were already soldiers, wounded and unfit for duty, or dead. Physically, the new trainees were either too young or too old to serve and survive in the infantry.

Driven out of Russia and Belarus and defeated in Italy and France, with cities and villages in Germany now suffering bombing and infantry attacks, the German army was hemorrhaging. Stefan's job was to transfuse the army with trained new blood. The battle lines had dramatically shifted. Pushed back from their offense deep in Russian territory, they were now defending German borders. Yet the delusion, believed by many soldiers, was that Germany was winning the war. How was that possible?

He strode toward the Slovakian *Ersatzdivisionen* barracks while the red and gold leaves of fall swirled along the path. His boots had worn through from marching, training soldiers, running ammunition, and fighting. They did little to protect his feet from the damp, cold earth. As he walked, Stefan shook his head, wondering for the thousandth time what he was doing—being a soldier. He was a farmer and a shopkeeper. Plucked from Scheindorf, Hungary, over two long years ago, he had left his wife without a husband and his children without their father. All he had ever wanted was to be a good provider and create a better life for his children than he had growing up. War had robbed him of his youth. He felt much older than nearly thirty years.

War was a thief that had stolen all that was precious.

He took a deep breath to steady his heart and looked across the camp. The acreage, once an expansive horse farm, had been commandeered and converted into a training facility. The rolling hills and once-peaceful pastoral setting had become a place for making war, dotted with houses converted into barracks, horse barns, the officers' quarters, and a mess hall. He wondered what the setting might have looked like before the war muddied the paths, leveled the crops, displaced the families that lived and worked there, and put the horses in jeopardy in battle. Everywhere he turned, he saw the damage of war. He hated it.

His thoughts drifted back to home, some nine hundred kilometers away. His heart beat with constant worry about his family. There had been no news from Maria for weeks. She was the love of his life and the fuel for his ambition. Were the girls okay? His youngest was just a baby when he left. He had only seen her a few times. His chest was heavy with concern. He should be taking care of them. The duality of duty—would it ever end?

The day suddenly darkened, and he looked up to see the sun hide behind a line of clouds. The bright afternoon quickly turned gray and cold as the wind picked up. The farmer-turned-soldier took a deep breath and smelled the mold of decaying leaves and the crisp scent of snow. It would not be long until snow would blanket the hills with deceptive white. Another winter would hold the country in its icy grip, killing without reason, more powerful than guns. War and winter—he could hardly win against one, let alone both.

Stefan turned up the collar of his coat against the chill and cinched his belt one notch tighter. It was the last notch. He entered the shelter of the barracks and quickly shouldered the door closed against the brisk wind. He removed his service cap, ran a hand through his thinning brown hair, and headed for the second-floor radio room. The Russians were invading all of Eastern Europe, plundering cities and villages. Germany was retreating. Was his family safe? Were they still in Scheindorf? He felt helpless. He was in agony waiting—he should be doing something. He vaulted the stairs two at a time, anxious for news.

He walked into the smoke-filled room. A cluster of veteran soldiers, many with war injuries, huddled around the radio receiver. They were listening to *Deutschlandsender*, Radio Germany's vast vehicle for propaganda, broadcast to every corner of Europe. He had heard that the transmission tower in Brandenburg, outside of Berlin, was the world's second largest structure after New York's Empire State Building. Was that true or just another lie?

Balding Stabsgefreiter Johann Schmidt looked up at Stefan, finished his half-smoked cigarette, and said, "Stefan, where've you been? Reading letters from home?"

Stefan glared at him. Their eyes met. They both knew the truth.

"Tough night?" Johann said.

Stefan nodded. "I'm sorry. I don't want to talk about it."

Johann arched an eyebrow and gestured to an empty seat. "Come, sit."

Stefan pulled up the chair and sat. He reached into his tunic, slipped out a pack of cigarettes, and lit one. He inhaled deeply. "No letters," he said, shaking his head and exhaling a smoke-filled sigh. "It's been three weeks. My wife, Maria, she writes almost every day. I don't know what has happened to them. I don't know if they are still in our village—if the Russians have come— or if they have left."

He paused and looked straight at Johann.

"I need to know."

The radio came to life with a baritone singing *"Berlin Bleibt doch Berlin"* ("Berlin Is Still Berlin"). The music faded, and the deep male voice of a seasoned radio announcer began the broadcast with, "Now the news of October 8."

The men leaned in closer to the radio, and the room fell quiet.

"Hostile action continues north of the Belgian city of Antwerp as elements of the British Second Army sustained heavy losses. Reichsführer Heinrich Himmler, on an inspection tour of the western front, assured our valiant troops the enemy will soon be conquered."

The men looked up and shook their heads in disbelief. They knew better.

The announcer continued, "On another note, we say farewell to one of our Führer's most loyal men, General der Infanterie Rudolf Schmundt. The general died of injuries he received on July 20 during the cowardly and futile plot to assassinate our Führer. Buried with full military honors, he was awarded the German Order for the highest duties to the state and party. The general now rests in a hero's cemetery of the Invalidenfriedhof. He was forty-eight. Moving on to the eastern front, two Panzer divisions have come to the aid of the Hungarian third army as the Red army drive stalls near Arad on the border of Hungary and Romania."

Schmidt spoke over the broadcast. "Stefan, that's near your village in the Satu Mare area, isn't it?"

Stefan nodded. Fear for his family's safety flooded through him.

The radio announcer continued in an upbeat voice, "Turning now to sports, rival Swedish middle-distance runners Gunder Hägg and Arne Andersson close in on their attempts to break the four-minute mile."

Stefan looked around the group and reached for the

dial. "Does anyone object? I need to hear the truth—not this nonsense."

"Go ahead," said Senior Lance Corporal Schmidt. "Someone watch the door. We don't want to get shot for treason."

"I'll watch the door." Corporal Becker stood up. "I've already lost an eye. Don't need to lose my head. Damned German propaganda! Find some real news, will you Stefan?"

When everyone was seated again, Stefan paused before searching for the new station. He surprised himself by sharing his thoughts. "Becker," Stefan looked at the Corporal. "That reminds me of something my father said the last time I was home. I can't get it out of my head. Pop said, 'You can't wrap lies in a pretty box and call it the truth. That's propaganda.'"

Schmidt angrily spit out his words. "Germany has hidden behind denial and lies. It's time for truth. We're fighting blind for what cause? Hitler's personal agenda?"

Stefan's heart hammered in his chest. As he reached for the dial with his right hand, his fingers did not respond. The cold damp night had exacerbated the throbbing phantom pain of his missing trigger finger. He shook his hand in frustration. Then reached for the dial with his left hand, quickly reduced the volume, and searched for the BBC's *Feindsender* station, the banned German-language reports that emanated from the enemy radio station in London.

Over the course of the broadcast, the German corporals learned that what they had already guessed was true. Following landings in Normandy earlier in the spring, British, French, Canadian, and American forces had blazed a trail across Western Europe. The German losses were in the hundreds of thousands—not just soldiers but civilians. Cities were being bombed and villages plundered. The Red army, aided by Czechoslovakian troops, was making gains in northeastern Slovakia. They could be here, at this training camp, in a matter of days. German and Soviet forces, locked in bitter fighting across eastern Hungary, were battling for the city of Debrecen.

Stefan's heart sank. If Debrecen was a target, the Red army could have already overrun the Hungarian village of Scheindorf, the home of Stefan's parents, his wife, and their two young daughters.

Judge Stefan Revak Senior, mayor of Scheindorf, slept deeply beside his wife.

A sound woke him.

He shot up in bed, instantly awake and alert. The room was cold and dark. *What was that?*

There—someone was pounding on the door. He threw off the heavy green quilt and quickly put on his shoes, wrapping himself in a blanket.

"What is it?" Gertrude whispered.

"Stay here."

Gertrude sat up in bed, grabbed her robe at the foot of the bed, and got up.

"You might need me," she said. "Or Maria and the girls might need me."

He saw the hard look in her dark eyes and the determined set of her jaw that he knew so well. Shaking his head, he smiled briefly in surrender. He could see still see the shadow of the beauty that had first attracted him—

that flash of spirit in her eyes. After thirty years of marriage, she was still more than his match, driven, intelligent, and hardworking—always a step ahead of him.

"I don't have time to argue with you," he said. "Just stay safe and listen."

He quickly left the bedroom and walked down the hall to the stairs. Out the window, he saw distant flashes of light illuminating the darkness. *Artillery?* He thought he heard rumbling in the distance, and his mind considered the possibilities as he walked down the stairs.

The senior Stefan opened the door. What he saw made his heart race.

A German army officer stood tall on the doorstep, ramrod straight in his olive-green field uniform. His cold blue eyes met Stefan's.

"*Welches Dorf ist das?*"

"This town is Scheindorf. My name is Revak. I'm the mayor," Stefan responded in German. Stefan judged that the officer was in his forties, older than his son was. His uniform, dotted with dried blood and smudged with dirt, bore the telltale signs of field combat.

"Are you German?" the officer asked.

"Yes, German Catholic."

"What about the people of this town? Are they German?"

Stefan hesitated. What did this officer want? He was much wiser since his son's last furlough. He looked the officer straight in the eyes, but the officer briefly looked away, distracted by a sound in the distance. When he looked back, Stefan saw exhaustion carved into the wrinkles around the man's eyes. Looking closer, he sensed fear.

The man's question disturbed him: *Are they German?*

Stefan felt the burden of his role; he was the shepherd of Scheindorf. The village was a melting pot of people and cultures, friends and family. They had come from all over Europe—most from Germany, but from Austria, Hungary, and Slovakia too, to build the first farming settlement generations ago. He had joyfully attended their weddings, celebrated the births of their children, and stood in sorrow by their graves.

There were Jews among them. Stefan knew of the roundup of Jews in other villages, the yellow stars that branded them sewn to their clothes, the stories of work camps and death and Jewish children left orphaned. Nothing like this had happened to Scheindorf—yet.

He chose his words carefully.

"Yes, most of us are of German descent."

The officer took off his cap and tucked it under his arm. His dark hair, threaded with streaks of gray, grazed the collar of his uniform.

"We are the Reich's Second Squadron, Cavalry Regiment 52." He gestured behind him. "We need shelter— immediately."

A hundred thoughts ran through Stefan's head. The soldiers were on the run. His son's prediction was coming true. What would happen to the village? Where was his son?

"Understood. What do you need?"

"We have some one hundred and fifty horses that need water and cover."

"We'll guide you through the forest. There is a nearby stream. We have barns for your men."

The officer shook his head. "The forest will work; the barns will only work to treat the wounded. We will feed and water the horses. We would welcome any food you can offer. Then we must leave. The Soviets have overrun our positions and will soon be here. Everyone must leave—the sooner the better. You must go west into Hungary, maybe even Austria."

Stefan's heart raced. How could the war come so close? So quickly?

"How is this possible?" His heart sank as he considered the pain of uprooting people's lives. "We have sick people, families, young children—women due to give birth. We are not prepared. We have livestock. There are nearly a thousand people in Scheindorf. Many have lived here for generations."

The officer's eyes flashed a warning. "If you value your life and the lives of your loved ones, you must leave. The Russians are animals. They will rape the women and girls. Anyone who can work will be shipped to Siberia to work in the mines. If you cannot work, you will be shot. Do you understand?"

Stefan's mind reeled. His heart hammered. "I understand."

"I think you do," the officer responded. "Warn the town at first light. I'll come back to check on you as soon as I get the men and the horses settled." He gave a curt nod and turned to leave. He stopped in midstride and turned back to Stefan. "What did you say your name was?"

"My name is Judge Stefan Revak." Stefan paused and then proudly said, "I have a son, also named Stefan. He is away, serving in the German army. His wife and daughters live here with us."

The officer smiled. "It is an honor." He bowed his head briefly. Then he reached out to shake Stefan's hand. "I am Hauptmann Georg Müller. At your service."

PART I

CHAPTER ONE

"What lies behind us and what lies before us are tiny matters compared to what lies within us."
Ralph Waldo Emerson

Scheindorf, Satu Mare, Romania
April 1922

SEVEN-YEAR-OLD Stefan Revak struggled under the weight of the manure cart, easing it through the ruts in the muddy road, his boots slipping and sinking in the muck. The worn cart creaked and groaned with every turn of the wooden wheels. The morning was sunny and bright, and blades of spring-green grass sprouted out between piles of dirty brown melting snow. Stefan's stomach rumbled, and he badly needed water to quench his thirst, but every moment that passed turned the road into a river of mud. He had several more loads to deliver to his Uncle Anton Revak before the road became impassable. There was no time to waste with eating or drinking.

Stefan was happy to be spending time with his uncle on this Saturday, even though he was moving manure, a daily chore at home too. Before and after school with

Herr Schradi, a Hungarian war veteran, Stefan would haul the cart of manure and spread it on his parents' fields. Later, he would plow it under to enrich the poor white-clay soil. Since his was father away working in America, he and his mother, Gertrude, did most of the chores around the farm. School was a break from the never-ending work. Since his family spoke German at home, the German, Romanian, and Hungarian classes were so easy that sometimes Stefan found himself dozing off.

Finally, he reached the place where Uncle Anton was making bricks for the village homes, combining clay and sand with manure and then letting them bake in the sun. Stefan sighed with relief, dropped the handles of the cart to the ground, and reached into his pocket to pull out a red kerchief, one of his mother's old babushkas. He wiped his face with the damp cloth and reached for the jug of water Anton passed him. Stefan drank deeply.

"I'll fill it up the water and bring you more with the next load," Stefan said smiling up at his uncle. He reminded him so much of his father—what he could remember. His father had been in America for two years. He was only five when he left.

Stefan swallowed hard, suddenly lonely. Anton was tall like his brother, with dark hair. Stefan's gaze connected with his uncle's kind gray eyes. They looked huge magnified by his rimless eyeglasses.

"Missing your father, aren't you?" Anton placed a firm, warm hand on Stefan's shoulder.

Stefan looked down, embarrassed. His eyes had begun to fill with tears. At seven, he was too old to cry. He would not feel sorry for himself.

He kept his head down and whispered, "Yes, I miss

my father."

Anton dropped down on one knee, slipped his finger under Stefan's chin, lifted his head, and looked deeply into the young boy's eyes.

Stefan stood up straight.

"Your father is working hard to get you and your mother to America. You need to work hard to help your mother here. Farmland is valuable. We make sacrifices in life for those things that are important. Your father is making a sacrifice by living away from you and your mother. You are making sacrifices by being the man of the house, taking care of your mother and the land. I'm sure your father is lonely, just like you. I know he must miss you. I can't imagine not watching my children grow up—and he's missing his only child."

Tears misted his uncle's eyes.

Perhaps seven wasn't too old for tears after all.

"But it's been so long since we've heard from him," Stefan replied.

Anton smiled. "When he sees you again, he'll be proud of his son—proud of the boy who works like a man."

Anton gave him a quick hug. Stefan felt warm on the inside. He fought back tears and found his smile.

"I'd better get going. The road's turning into a river of mud."

"That's my boy!" Anton smiled, patted him on the shoulder, and turned back to his piles of bricks. Then he stopped and called out before Stefan could leave. "Oh, wait."

Anton walked over to a pile of clothing and reached into his rucksack. "I promised your mother a bottle of my best schnapps—payment for your work." He held out the bottle. "Come, take it back with you."

"But I'm not finished yet."

"Take it now while I still have it." Anton smiled and winked.

Stefan understood. He walked over, took the bottle from his uncle, and carefully placed it in the cart.

He turned back to his uncle. "I wish she didn't like this so much."

"I think she drowns her sorrows in drink," Anton said.

"She's different when she doesn't drink. I know she's sad all the time, but when she doesn't drink, she's—" Stefan stopped to search for the words.

"She's kinder?" Anton offered.

Stefan nodded, once again embarrassed. Uncertain of what to say, he said good-bye, picked up the handles of the cart, and headed back down the road toward home at the opposite end of town.

As he pushed the empty cart through town, the steeple bell of St. Anne's Catholic Church chimed eleven bells. The bell and his stomach signaled it was time to eat. His mother had told him the bell was a gift from the bishop, given to the village in 1864, long before Stefan was born. St. Anne was the patron saint of the village. Sometimes before Mass, his mother would kneel at the statue of St. Anne. She would make the sign of the cross, hold her rosary, and whisper prayers. Sometimes she would bow her head and cry. He never let her catch him watching. She would be embarrassed.

Father Johann Ettinger, the priest, tall and skinny in his black cassock, was out sweeping the church steps. He looked up, saw Stefan, and waved. Stefan waved back. Father Ettinger was always happy, it seemed.

On his journey home, Stefan passed the cobbler's shop of Blasius Schimpf, one of Scheindorf's two shoe-makers. He heard the clang of metal on metal as he passed the blacksmith shop. The door to the general store opened, and two children raced out joyfully holding small bags of sweets high above their heads, with their mother not far behind them calling, "Wait for lunch! No sweets till after lunch!" She reached for the bags in vain; the children darted away from her grasp.

Stefan smiled.

He looked down at the cart, stinking from manure, and sighed. No sweets for him. Being the only child and a boy, there was no time in his short life when he was not working.

Passaic, New Jersey
The United States of America
April 1922

While young Stefan Revak hauled manure, his father walked to work on the last day of his workweek, Saturday. It had been another long week, and he was tired. He could already smell the fumes from the dye and the wet wool from Forstmann Worsted Mills, and it was still two kilometers away. Stefan was fortunate. He was one of the twenty-five million immigrants who had entered the United States between 1890 and 1920, and he had quickly found work. He was pleased to work at the well-known factory, founded in 1904 by German entrepreneurs from Flanders in Belgium. The family was one of the oldest in the weaver's guild. Their business was booming with the American demand for wool and worsted garments.

The walk to work gave him time to think—and worry. How much longer would it take to save up enough money to bring Gertrude and Stefan to America? The wages were good, better than most, and he put away every penny he could. It had been two years, and still he had not saved enough to book their passage to America. He was lonely and tired. He'd come to America to give his family a better life in the country where dreams come true. Now an ocean separated them.

Three of his brothers, Johan, Josef, and Michael, already had their wives with them here. He paid Johan a little money for food and rent every month. It was the least he could do, but that made his saving slow.

Today, he was discouraged. Dyeing wool was hard work; the shifts were twelve hours long. The stench from the formaldehyde used to set the dye, was so overpowering it made men dizzy. The sour chemical odor clung to his clothes and dried his hands so much they looked like wrinkled prunes. The smell lingered on his skin, even after he scrubbed himself clean. What would Gert think? He was working with embalming fluid!

There was no time to look for another job, one that might pay more. His English was not very good—better than when he had arrived two years ago, but not good enough for many jobs. His only day off was Sunday. No one worked on Sunday. Nothing was open. Sunday was for church—and for family.

He took a deep breath. As he walked, he watched couples, their heads bowed in close conversation, some followed by chaperones. The gigantic Dutch elm trees that lined each side of the street formed an arch, and green buds of new life dotted the branches. The humidity was rising, and he looked up to see a blue sky with tall gray clouds that promised rain. The April day smelled of spring—if you could sort through the manure left by the horses—but that too brought him back to thoughts of home. It was time for enriching the fields and getting ready to sow. How was Gertrude doing? He needed to write her more frequently, but the days flew by, and every night he fell into bed exhausted. But tomorrow was Sunday. He would write tomorrow.

Sunday dawned bright and sunny. As was his routine, Stefan walked to the train station, wearing his brown hat, a clean white shirt and tie, and his only suit, a "second" from the factory. He planned to catch the early train to New York City to visit the Pfitzner family: Rosalia, Gertrude's sister; her husband, Adolf; and their daughter, Helen. He hoped his brothers would join them also. He wondered if Rosalia would have news of Gertrude—it had been so long since he had heard from her. Sometimes he envied their good fortune, being together as a family in America. He pushed the thought down deep and replaced the feeling of loss with one of gratitude that he had family close by who shared their homes with him.

The morning was cool, but with not a cloud in the sky, he could sense a hot day coming. The station already bustled with families, carrying baskets of food and flowers, dressed up for picnics and visits with relatives. Trains whistled loud, shrill warnings, and their smokestacks spewed black and gray billows of coal dust. He admired the women dressed in their Sunday best with their wide-brimmed hats, parasols for providing shade from the sun, and colorful silk skirts that rustled as they walked.

His constant sense of disappointment clouded the otherwise beautiful day. He knew this was what Gertrude wanted: to be fashionably dressed up in fine clothes, attend parties and the theater, have a regular dinner with her family—to sit at a table with china and silver. He felt guilty, enjoying these simple pleasures while his wife managed livestock, tended a farm, and raised their only child.

He boarded the train, found a seat by the window, and pulled out paper and a pen.

Dearest Gertrude, my Love,

I am on the train to visit Rosalia, so my pen may waver on the page from time to time.

Though I'm grateful for the work, the hours are long—no longer than you are working, I know. I wish you were here. I miss you terribly.

Helen is growing into a lovely young woman. Her voice is beautiful! She sings for us after dinner. Her proud parents feel that with the right training, she is destined for the opera.

Helen takes care of a little American boy. His name is Tom. He is about Stefan's age. Watching him every week makes me realize how much I am missing—not seeing Stefan every day—watching him grow up. I go along with Helen and Tom to the park after dinner every Sunday. I am teaching Tom German. He is helping me learn English.

I have been saving every penny so that you can book passage here for you and Stefan. I will not send it until I

*have enough for your tickets. How is Stefan? How are you?
I feel so helpless, so far away. But we will be together soon.
Please do not give up hope. I will find a way.*

Please write to me.

Love,

Stefan

———•———

The dinner at Rosalia and Adolf's was a true respite from work. The boisterous extended family crowded around the long narrow dining room table. Today was the day for bringing out the few treasures the families had been able to bring with them from Europe. The table, covered with a lovely cream lace tablecloth, had a crystal bowl of pink cherry blossoms in the center and was set with Gertrude's favorite family china, Spode Buttercup.

The smells from the kitchen made Stefan's mouth water. Rosalia came out with the food: first, a platter of sliced roast lamb with mint jelly; then a bowl of boiled new potatoes swimming in butter, sprinkled with fresh parsley harvested from the potted herb garden she nurtured in the sunroom. There were carrots sweet with honey and thyme, pickled cucumbers, and a basket of warm, freshly baked dinner rolls.

The conversation around the table was lively, catching up on what had happened during the week, politics in America, and the hardships in Germany after the Great War.

"Have you heard about this man Adolf Hitler?" Josef asked Stefan.

"Not sure if I have," Stefan said. He had heard about Hitler, but he wanted to hear his brothers' points of view before joining into the conversation.

"Well, evidently he's a war hero—earned the Iron Cross during the Great War—and he's giving speeches, encouraging the people of Germany, talking about getting back our pride and honor—"

"He's speaking in beer halls—to drunks," Michael interrupted.

"Well, at least someone is trying to get Germany back on its feet!" Josef said.

"He's a maniac," Michael said. "Delusional. We're blinded by our need for a hero—a savior."

"Germany needs leadership to recover from the war," said Josef. "It has been too long already."

"But just any kind of leader? Have you read any of his speeches? He is more about himself and his glory than the greater good of Germany."

There was silence at the table.

"He frightens me," said Michael.

Stefan listened with interest. Everyone knew of Germany's economic and psychological devastation after the Great War. They had been defeated for the first time in a century. Was this man's message truly one of hope? Or was he just a politician thirsty for power and prestige? The war-torn country was vulnerable to politicians who made promises they could never keep.

"Are you coming with me this afternoon?" Helen asked Stefan from across the table.

Distracted, Stefan smiled at his young niece. "After this meal, I really need a walk."

"Wonderful," Helen replied. "I know that Tom is looking forward to seeing you and practicing his German with you."

"If only I could pick up English as quickly as Tom picks up German."

"He soaks it up like a sponge, doesn't he?" Helen replied, laughing.

"His accent is perfect," Stefan replied.

"He sounds just like you!" Helen laughed again. "A little you! You are teaching him your dialect."

"It's the only one I know," Stefan said, smiling back and shrugging his shoulders. Her laughter helped him forget his own frustrations with language and money for a moment.

"Don't forget the apple strudel I made for dessert," Rosalia said.

"Never, never would I forget that!" Stefan smiled. "You are a marvelous cook, Rosalia! Thank you for opening your home to me."

"Someday, my sister will be here too, yes?"

"Yes," Stefan said. Tears pricked at his eyes. His heart felt a little sad and guilty that he was enjoying the day so much.

<hr />

When Stefan walked out on the front porch after dinner, Helen and Tom were waiting at the foot of the stairs. He put his hat on his head, walked down slowly, and smiled at the scene.

Tom was wearing a crisp white shirt with a square collar, finished with a loosely tied dark blue bow. He had on long white socks tucked into navy blue knickers, with shiny black patent leather shoes. On his head was a white sailor's cap.

Tom stood up straight and gave Stefan a snappy salute.

"Ready for duty, sir," Tom said.

Stefan was not sure what to say. "Ready for your German class?" he managed to say in English with a heavy German accent.

"Yes, sir!"

Stefan smiled at the miniature soldier.

"I'm going to be an officer in the United States navy, just like my father," Tom said.

Stefan's heart swelled with fatherly pride—even though he did not know Tom's father, he understood the importance of a father's example for his son. *Who was the example for his son?* Once again, Stefan's conscience pricked with guilt.

"I'm sure you will be a fine officer," Stefan responded in German.

Tom frowned.

"Don't understand?" Stefan replied.

Tom shook his head.

"Well, let's walk—and Helen will help us translate together," Stefan said.

Tom looked up at Stefan with big, trusting eyes and reached up for his hand. Stefan's heart tugged again. He took Tom's little hand on one side and Helen on the other and they walked to the park, talking all the way.

———

Young Stefan wheeled the empty cart back home for one last load of manure. Gertrude opened the front door and flew out, her white apron flapping in the wind.

"Did you get the schnapps?" she demanded.

He looked up at her but did not meet her eyes. He had been hoping to avoid this conversation, or at least delay it until later in the day.

"Not yet, Mama," he lied. "After I deliver the last load . . . I'll get it then."

"Come home straight away then," she said.

"Uncle Anton promised me lunch. I'll eat, then come home straight away. Okay, Mama?" He watched her face fall with disappointment.

She nodded. "It's okay." She managed a little smile. "Don't eat them out of house and home."

His heart lifted a little. He loved his mother. "I won't."

"And don't forget to thank your aunt—and say hello from me. Okay?"

"I won't," he said. "See you later, Mama."

Stefan leaned into the cart and rolled it toward the manure pile. Once he reached it, he looked back toward the house. His mother had gone back inside. Sighing in relief, he took the bottle of schnapps and hid it inside the hollow of a dead tree. It worried him when his mother drank. She never seemed to know when to stop. He wondered if it was because she was sad. He had tasted schnapps once, and it gave him a splitting headache.

He picked up the shovel and started piling the last load of manure into the cart. He was thirsty, and his stomach growled with hunger. *Almost done.* When the last of the manure filled the cart, he lifted up the handles and heaved it one more time back to Uncle Anton's.

Rolling the cart once again through the village, he

saw his teacher, tall and skinny Herr Schradi, shaking a bony finger at two of his classmates. He stifled a laugh. Herr Schradi reminded Stefan of a scarecrow. As he watched, one of the boys tried to make a run for it, and the teacher quickly reached out and grabbed him by the collar, dragging him back for an impromptu lecture. It did not matter what day of the week, in class or out of class, the teacher was a stern disciplinarian.

Stefan ducked his head down, hoping he could pass unnoticed. Herr Schradi, intent on scolding his young pupils, did not see Stefan pass by.

Stefan sighed. He was tired. He felt filthy, grimy from the work. He could taste salt as the sweat rolled down his face and burned his eyes. He smelled like manure. He thought of the children with their bag of sweets and his mother with her schnapps, and his heart filled with worry. Work had to be done. He was the man of his household.

Finally, he rolled the final load to his uncle's field. Anxious to eat, he quickly shoveled the manure into a pile. His stomach ached with hunger. His Aunt Anna was a great cook, and there was always plenty of food to go around. He could taste the rich, creamy mushroom gravy she sometimes made with schnitzel, the sauerkraut with its sweet bite, and the sausages—just the thought of her cooking made him salivate. He wondered if she would have made apple crisp, the warm apples, soft and sweet, with a crunchy topping. How he craved that sweet at the end of the meal. No matter how much he ate!

"Stefan, come on . . . lunch is ready!" Uncle Anton called from the porch. "Use the pump and clean up. I've left a towel and some soap there. Don't forget to leave your shoes at the door."

Stefan nodded and waved. Once, driven by his hunger and lured by the smell of sausage, he had run into the house wearing his filthy, manure-caked shoes. Aunt Anna had thrown a fit.

The smell of the hot food drifted through the open windows of the house. His stomach rumbled in anticipation. Beads of sweat ran down his face and back as he quickly primed the pump, and clear, cold well water gushed out. He put his head under the pump and let the icy water run over his hair and face. It felt so good he could have stayed there forever, but he was starving. He grabbed the soap, splashed water on his face, and scrubbed off the grime as quickly as he could. He hurried, drying his face and hands on the run as he leaped up the three stairs to the porch. He dropped his muddy shoes on the porch and went in.

The family of five sat on wooden benches that flanked a long table. Aunt Anna softly hummed a little song as she laid out the feast: hot bean soup, warm black rye bread with a crock of butter, homemade pickles, fresh cheese curds, and sliced *blutwurst*. His mouth watered as he found an empty place on a bench and slipped in. He watched as his youngest cousin, Margaret Maria, reached out, stuck a little finger into the cheese curds, and took a quick taste. He caught her eye and smiled—her secret safe.

Stefan looked at his aunt and smiled. He thought she was pretty. She had big dark eyes and long brown hair that she had braided down her back. She was wearing a bright blue dress with a white apron, and she always seemed to be smiling. Stefan's mother almost never smiled. Before she sat down, Aunt Anna picked up a towel and waved it in front of her flushed face to cool off.

"It's hot by the oven," she said.

Suddenly, he remembered his mother's advice.

"Thank you for lunch," he said.

Aunt Anna beamed down at him. "You are very welcome, Stefan. Thank you for helping us."

Her kind smile warmed his heart.

"Let's say a short prayer and then eat," his uncle said.

Stefan bowed his head. Anton read a passage from the book of Timothy praising the Lord for his goodness and giving thanks for the food they were about to eat. Stefan thought the words were fine and good but much too long. It seemed the passage would never end. It finally did.

He took a piece of warm bread, slathered it with the creamy butter, and savored the dense, earthy bite of the rye. The bowls of food went around the table until they were scraped clean. Everyone was laughing and happy, sated with the heavy food. Stefan wanted to lick the bowls to capture every morsel but knew his mother would be disappointed in him if she heard about it. He did not want to risk her anger.

After a dessert of baked apples and thick cream, it was time to say good-bye. Stefan thanked his aunt and uncle again and headed home.

CHAPTER TWO

"You gain strength, courage, and confidence by every experience in which you really stop to look fear in the face. You are able to say to yourself, 'I have lived through this horror. I can take the next thing that comes along.' You must do the thing you think you cannot do."

Eleanor Roosevelt

GERTRUDE WORKED IN the garden, turning the heavy, wet soil with a pitchfork, then breaking up the clumps with a hoe. She mixed cow manure with the rocky, white-clay soil to create a richer environment for the kitchen crops that would sustain them over the summer and fall. Soon the earth would be warm enough to plant. In a few weeks, their reward would be green sprouts, then the bounty of cabbage, carrots, peas, beans, and potatoes.

She paused in her work and took a long drink of cool water from the brown earthen jar. Putting the jar down, she hitched up her skirt so it would not drag in the dirt, and leaned on the pitchfork to take a brief rest. Her hands ached. She rubbed them together, massaging her knuckles to ease the pain. It was a never-ending cycle of work, much the same day after day, changing only with the seasons. Her exhaustion brought tears of self-pity to her eyes, and loneliness filled her heart.

How did this happen? Her mind wandered back. *Where have the years gone?* Here she was, nearly thirty years old, with a husband in America for over two years, a young son to care for, and a house, livestock, and a farm to run all on her own. She would be old before her time. It was not supposed to be like this. This was not the plan.

She remembered her excitement when, as a young girl of sixteen, she had boarded a ship bound for New York City. Her trunk, carefully packed, held her treasured white lace embroidered blouses and tailored skirts, clothes her father had bought for her from the Czechoslovakian clothing label Nehera. Her heart overflowed with hopes, dreams, and the promise of a new life in a foreign land. She left everything that was familiar—Stefan, her then-boyfriend; her family; her language—for the promised land of America. She worked as a governess, becoming a part of a new family, loving the thrill of the bustling city, watching the women and men in their stylish clothes, and enjoying the many things to see and do. She carefully saved her wages. Three years later, she came back to her village to marry Stefan.

She remembered it like it was yesterday. She had returned to Satu Mare young, hopeful, and innocent. She was even more in love with Stefan than ever, her feelings deepened by distance and knowing that he was the only one for her. She did not intend to stay in Romania. Neither of them did. They would go to America, find jobs, work hard, and save to build a new life.

They married within the month. Soon she was pregnant, and they were thrilled. But their excitement turned to crushing disappointment when they learned that pregnant women could not immigrate to the United States.

In 1917, when her son was nearly three, her dreams were dashed again when the Great War halted immigration to the United States entirely. That year an August fire raged through Scheindorf. The thatched roofs of barns and homes were tinder during the dry summer; some nineteen homes and fifteen barns burned to the ground. Though their home was spared, the village needed rebuilding.

Gertrude surveyed the kitchen garden, empty but for a pile of manure and her tools. It seemed like Stefan had left for America a lifetime ago—yet it was only two years. *This was not the plan,* she thought again.

She needed a drink—not of water. Schnapps was her only escape from the life she had been given.

What did Papa used to say?

"You have to take things the way they come."

Why? She was angry and frustrated. *Why should I have to live like this? Oh God, when will you hear my prayers?*

"Mama, I'm back!"

Startled by her son's voice, Gertrude's heart fell, and she was flooded with embarrassment. Had he seen her cry?

She reached for her *taschentuch* and briefly blew her nose, turning away to hide the tears. She did not want Stefan to see her this way. She took in a few deep breaths and turned to him, her gruff voice hiding her sorrow.

"We've got work to do here. Did you bring the schnapps?"

She saw him flinch a little. He looked down and kicked the dirt, stalling. She caught his look but dismissed it. She needed a drink. She did not expect a seven-year-old to understand.

"Well?"

"Yes, Mama—I've got it."

"Then where is it? Go and get it. Bring it home. Then we have some plowing to do. Off with you—don't dawdle."

She saw a look of disappointment on his face, almost a look of sadness, and her heart softened. She reached out for his arm.

"Did you have a good lunch?" Pulling him close, she smelled sweat and manure. Her son, the worker. She pulled back. "My goodness, we need to wash your clothes. I hope your aunt didn't mind too much."

"I washed up—as best I could—before lunch. Left my shoes on the porch."

"Good boy." She smiled at the sight of him. His face had been scrubbed as clean as he could get it, but dirt lined the edges of his hair, and he had missed a big smudge on the bridge of his nose.

"I do smell, don't I?" Stefan smiled at her.

A laugh escaped from her lips, and she smiled back. Love filled her heart.

"It's hard on both of us, you know, without your father. I hate to see you growing up without him in your life. He's a good man. I can't fill his shoes."

She was surprised when Stefan reached out and wrapped his arms around her waist. She looked down at him. He looked up at her.

"We can do it, Mama. We'll take care of everything."

She sighed and looked at her small boy, the earnest look on his face, hair caked with dirt. Her heart tugged, and her eyes brimmed with tears. With his skinny arms locked around her waist, she dared not cry.

She took a deep breath and found a small reserve of strength.

"Yes, we can and will do it." She smiled and looked in his dark brown eyes, the first good look at her son in a while. He was growing so fast. Lean from hard work, he was getting taller by the month. "You look so much like your father. Soon you'll be the age I met him." She met his eyes.

"I'll get the plow ready for us," he said.

"You're a good boy."

———•◆•———

Stefan was too small to manage the old plow, so he and his mother worked together to assemble it. The challenging physical routine was one they knew well. Gertrude and Stefan positioned the heavy plow blade behind the wooden wheeled cart. Then Stefan led two of their three cows, old Romanian Baltatas, from the barn.

"Come on, old girls," he pleaded, guiding them one by one into their yokes at the front of the cart. "It's better for you this way. You can pull, or I can eat you." He fastened the harness and checked to make sure all of the straps were tight and the cart and plow were tethered together.

Gertrude handed him a cloth bag. "There's a jug of water, some cheese, and a bit of bread. You'll be hungry before you're finished."

"Thanks, Mama," Stefan said. The lightness in his heart dampened at the sadness etched on his mother's face.

Stefan watched her walk back home, head down, her pace slow.

How long will we be alone?

Stefan shook off his worry. He had to guide the cows nearly two kilometers to reach the fields. He attached the cloth satchel of food to the wooden cart, took position behind the plow handles, dug his feet into the earth, and pushed, nudging the cart forward.

"Come on, girls—he who rests grows rusty!" One cow got the message and started to drag the other along. The ancient farming tool moved slowly.

The journey to the far-off field gave Stefan time to think again. He talked to the cows as they moved across the uneven, rocky soil: "Good girls. We'll do it, one day at a time. Papa will send for us. We'll be together again as a family. We can do this."

As Stefan worked, the only sounds he heard were the groaning of the wood planks of the cart, the creaking strain of the leather hitch, and the heavy breathing of the cows. The earth smelled rich, full of promise. He was alone—not a soul to be seen.

His thoughts strayed and he wondered how things would have been different if his father was home. His father would be helping with the work. He never wanted his children to have to live without a father. His mother would be happier. She would not drink so much. He remembered what Uncle Anton said: "She drowns her sorrow in drink." He never wanted his children to have to live in fear of their mother or her drinking. Life should not have to be so hard—or so lonely.

Stefan worked until midafternoon and then stopped to quench his thirst. The cows drank from a puddle of water in the field and nibbled on some new grass. He devoured the cheese and bread and drained the jug of water. He took some deep breaths and surveyed his work. So far he had plowed eight rows—four to go.

A flock of noisy sparrow hawks caught his attention. They were flying north—another sign of spring. The sky was a deep blue, and the sun was starting to sink lower in the sky, painting the sky and landscape a deeper blue. The temperature had already started to drop. It would be sunset soon.

He got up, tucked the jar and satchel in the cart, wiped the sweat from his face one more time, and went back to finish his work.

It was dark when Stefan settled the cows in the barn. He made sure they had sufficient hay and water. Then he checked on the chickens. All was well.

Tired and hungry, he walked up the steps to the porch and took off his boots, which were wet and covered with mud. They would dry overnight outside. He went into the kitchen and lit a candle. His stomach growled with hunger. There was a pot of vegetable soup still warm on the stove. It was not much, but it was more to eat than he had some days. His mother had left bread on the table with an apple.

He helped himself to the soup, rich with carrots, cabbage, and potatoes, and he noticed a few pieces of precious chicken meat floating in the broth. He sat down at the table, devoured the soup, and then soaked up every remaining drop with the bread. He held the apple in his hand, turning it over, and smiled thinking of

Uncle Anton and his schnapps. He bit into the apple, and the juice dripped down his chin. He wiped his sleeve across his mouth.

Stefan got up, rinsed the bowl with a pitcher of water on the sideboard, dried it, and put it back on the shelf. Then he went in search of his mother.

As he approached her room, he could hear her snoring. He held up the candle to look at her. She had fallen asleep in her dress and her apron. He put the candlestick down on her bedside table and searched for a blanket. It was so cold in the room he could see his breath. The empty bottle of schnapps was on the floor.

"Good night, Mama," he said as he covered her with a blanket.

He headed for his room. The bliss of sleep would come quickly. In a few hours, it would be Sunday morning. He would need to water and feed the chickens, collect the eggs, and milk the cow before washing and dressing for Mass. He quickly undressed, blew out the candle, and got into bed, pulling the covers up to his chin. He was asleep before he had time to worry about his mother.

CHAPTER THREE

*"The voyage of the best ship is a zigzag line of a
hundred tacks."*
Ralph Waldo Emerson

Passaic, New Jersey
Summer of 1922

STEFAN WALKED BRISKLY to the dock, trying to contain his excitement. It had been two long, lonely years of saving money to pay for Gertrude and Stefan's passage to New York City. Their dream was about to become reality. He thought he had enough, but since sending money was expensive, he wanted to make sure.

Stefan approached the open window of the ticket office.

"Good morning, sir," Stefan said and took off his hat. "Please excuse my poor English. Do you speak German by chance?"

The man in the ticket office smiled. "Yes, I speak German, a little French, and some Italian. What can I do for you?"

Stefan sighed in relief and continued the conversation in German.

"My wife and son are still in Romania. I think I have enough money to book passage for them from Bremerhaven, Germany, to New York. They will have to take a train there. How much are tickets now? Do you know Bremerhaven?" Stefan stopped talking. "I'm sorry," he said. "I'm sure you know the route."

Stefan had the money in a worn leather pouch. He took it out and passed it to the man.

"Is this enough?"

The man checked the ticket price and schedule and then counted Stefan's money.

"I'm sorry," he said. "The ticket price went up just last week. You're ten dollars short."

Stefan took a deep breath. Ten dollars would take him two more weeks to save. Would immigration still be open then? Immigration rules seemed to change by the month. He could not wait any longer.

He reached out and took the money, slipped it back into the pouch, and tucked it into his jacket pocket.

"Thank you," he said and turned to walk away.

"Maybe you could borrow the money?" the ticket man said.

Stefan turned back. He was trying desperately to keep his disappointment and fear at bay.

"I can try. My brothers live here. I can try."

"Well, good luck to you."

Stefan tipped his hat in farewell and walked away, his heart heavy. Gertrude would be devastated if she knew.

That Sunday at dinner, Stefan reluctantly asked his brother Michael for a loan. His brother had already done so much for him. He hated to ask—and the answer was not what he hoped. The brother had no savings to offer—his wife had been sick and out of work. They were living week to week. On Monday, he asked a couple of men he knew. Money was tight for them also; they had to think of their own families. He was desperate to get the money to Gertrude, but he could not see a way.

As he walked home from work that Monday, Stefan was deeply discouraged. The evening was soft and warm. He looked around and saw couples strolling together, some ducking into cozy, candlelit cafés for dinner. Parents walked with their children, who laughed and licked their dripping ice cream cones. One mother stopped, took out her handkerchief, quickly wet it on her tongue, and leaned down to wipe the chocolate-ringed mouth of her son. The child looked like his Stefan. It made him feel even lonelier. An ocean separated him from the people he loved most in the world, and he had no idea how to get them to America.

Stefan turned the corner and spotted Mr. Baum, a Jewish man from Germany, the shopkeeper of the corner store. The old man was sitting on a bench, his gray-bearded chin resting on his cane, watching the people go by. He saw Stefan and smiled.

"Good evening," Stefan said. He really did not want to talk. He did not want the man to notice his sadness. He stopped at the store every week and considered Mr. Baum a casual friend, but tonight his sorrow was his own.

"Stefan, it's a beautiful night! Isn't it?" The man gestured up to the sliver of a moon in the purple evening sky. "Oh, the linden trees," Mr. Baum continued. "See their star-shaped white blossoms? They smell like honey—and lemon. Don't they?"

Mr. Baum pointed up at the trees, and the blossoms fell to the ground like fragrant snowflakes.

"Yes, they do—I never noticed that before," Stefan said halfheartedly. His head dropped.

"Stefan, why are you so sad?"

Stefan took off his hat and shook his head. "Nothing ever goes the way you plan it—the way you want it to go," he said.

"What's bothering you? Tell me. Come over here, sit down." Mr. Baum moved over and patted the bench next to him. "Sit down. Talk to me."

Stefan sat down. "I really shouldn't say."

"It's okay, Stefan, you can talk to me. I am an old man; there isn't much I haven't heard before or been through. I've been through much."

Stefan sighed. "I need to send money home to my wife." He looked down at his hands while he talked. "I thought I had enough to bring my family here. I was wrong."

He paused to compose himself. Tears burned his eyes and choked his throat. He did not want to cry in front of the shopkeeper.

"I'm ten dollars short. I asked five or six guys—no one could help me."

Stefan got up to walk away. He knew it was not forever, this shortfall. He would earn the rest in two weeks. At this moment, the disappointment felt like a mortal blow. He had waited so long already.

"Stefan, let's talk for a bit," the shopkeeper said. "Come, sit back down. The nights are hard for me since my wife died."

The streetlight illuminated the kind man's lined face as he looked up at Stefan. Stefan saw the grief in his eyes and the loneliness they both shared.

He sat back down.

After a few minutes of talking and getting to know one another better, the shopkeeper stood up.

"Wait here. I need to go inside for a minute."

Stefan waited, feeling he had said too much.

The shopkeeper returned and held out ten dollars.

"Here's the money, Stefan. Send it to your wife."

Stefan's heart filled with gratitude. He could not believe the kindness of this man.

The next payday, Stefan went directly to the store and paid the money back.

———◆———

Young Stefan took his time walking home on the last day of the school year, meandering down the street on the warm afternoon. He was startled to see his mother running down the street toward him. He ran toward her, his heart leaping into his mouth. What had happened? Was it Uncle Anton?

His fear turned to surprise when he reached her and saw her smiling. She had tears in her eyes. She snatched him up in a tight embrace. She was trembling—not with pain but with joy.

"Oh, Stefan! We're going to America! My prayers have been answered!"

Her words came out rapidly. His ear was pressed so hard against her apron that her words were muffled, but he heard them all.

"I got a letter from your papa. He sent us the money to go to America."

Tears of relief filled Stefan's eyes. His mother used to talk about America, long ago when she was happy. The stories sounded like a fairy tale. She did not talk about it anymore.

She pushed him away and held him by the shoulders, beaming at him. "America is the most amazing place in the world," she said. "The people wear lovely clothes and eat in fancy restaurants, and the buildings are as tall as mountains."

"What does Papa say?"

"He says to sell everything—our house, the land, the livestock. We will use the money to take a train to Bremerhaven and then book passage to New York. My sister, Rosalia, and her husband will be our sponsors."

She stopped briefly to catch her breath and gave him a smile that lit up her face. He hardly recognized the woman before him. He had never seen her look this beautiful.

"Since your father already has a job, and we have sponsors, we'll sell everything, pack what we can carry, and say our good-byes." She ruffled his hair. "We just have to complete the necessary paperwork in Budapest."

Suddenly it seemed real to Stefan, and he felt a little dizzy—overwhelmed with the possibilities of leaving everything familiar. Would he feel lost among buildings as tall as mountains? And yet—his father would be there. "We're going to America? To be with Papa? It's true?"

"It's true," she said, and her eyes sparkled with hope for the first time in his memory.

Over the next few weeks, while Stefan tended the fields, weeding the early summer crops, his mother managed the Budapest immigration paperwork. Word of their departure traveled fast, and Stefan and his mother received several offers from nearby landowners to buy up their property. Land was always valuable, and Stefan and his mother had well-cared-for prime land to sell. Even Uncle Anton was interested in purchasing the cows and chickens. This was all good news.

The sun was setting when Stefan returned from the fields. The cows were in for the night, and he was hungry after a long day of work. He dropped his shoes on the porch and went into the house. It was unusually quiet, the kitchen empty. The only thing on the table was an envelope. Stefan picked it up. The stamps and seals looked official—*The Directorate for Migration and Nationality, Bucharest.*

Not knowing what to think, Stefan went to search for his mother. He heard muffled sobs from behind her bedroom door. He opened the door and found his mother on her bed, crying into her pillow. Sheets of paper littered the floor.

What was wrong? Had someone died?

He walked over to his mother's side.

"Mama, what's wrong?" he whispered.

She did not respond.

Alarmed, he put his hand on her shoulder and shook her. "Mama, what's wrong!"

After a moment, his mother finally sat up. Tears were streaming from her eyes. He passed her his handkerchief, and she blew her nose. She looked awful. Her eyes were red and puffy from crying, and her lips trembled. She could hardly catch her breath from the sobs that still wracked her slim frame.

Then she finally looked in his eyes. He saw desperation and fear, and his anxiety soared.

"We are not going to America," she said.

He could hardly believe it. "Mama, why?"

She sighed and looked up at him. "The United States has decided to slow down immigration. They are using a system to limit the number of people who enter the country. It's called a quota. I don't know exactly what it means, but it means that we are here—and your father is there. Once again, we are separated by an ocean."

She started to cry again.

He put his arms around her, and she sobbed into his shoulder.

"Mama, we have each other," Stefan said with false confidence. He had no idea what they would do now.

His mother reached out and brushed his hair back from his face. "You have become quite a little man. Your father will be very proud of you when he someday sees you. I doubt he will recognize you—you're getting so tall."

Stefan swallowed and waited.

Gertrude blew her nose into her handkerchief. She took a deep breath, and her sad eyes met Stefan's. Her voice was even and determined. "Tomorrow, we will go to see my papa. I need his advice. We will leave as soon as we can. After you tend the chickens, run over and see if Frau Schimpf can look after the cows and the chickens for a few days. Your school friend Martin can help her. We'll bring her back something from Opa's house to thank her."

Stefan nodded. He didn't remember his opa and oma very well—he had only seen them a couple of times. He knew they lived in the city of Satu Mare, some miles away.

"We can make it in a day if we start early," his mother said. She paused. "I need to go home."

———————

Stefan woke up early the next morning, anxious to do his chores and help his mother get ready for their journey. He thought about the news of yesterday. Though it had greatly upset his mother, living in Scheindorf was all he knew. Moving to America meant leaving Uncle Anton—the closest man to a father to him. If they left, he would miss his cousins and Aunt Anna. What if America was not as wonderful as they said? Would he make friends? Would it be hard to learn English? Would the children he met make fun of him because he was different? Stefan had more questions than answers, and he knew he could not talk to his mother about it.

He pushed his concerns about America aside and focused on the day ahead. He was excited to be doing something different besides weeding, hoeing, and plowing. Going to Satu Mare was an adventure

His mother was in the kitchen, hot water boiled on the stove. His breakfast of bread, butter, peach preserves, fresh warm milk, and an apple was on the table. She was wearing her travel clothes and a blue babushka. While he ate, she boiled the eggs and packed a rucksack with a loaf of black bread, apples, and the six eggs. He watched her move purposefully around the kitchen. Her eyes were still red and her posture stooped, but she gave him a small smile when he got up and cleared his place.

"It'll be all right, Mama," he said, trying to convince both his mother and himself.

She nodded. Tears started to slip from her eyes again. "Let's go. This is no time for tears." She shook her head, chiding herself. "We've got a long journey ahead."

Within minutes, they left the house and walked through town heading west. He tried to remember what his grandparents looked like. He remembered sweets and the smell of *sauerbraten*.

"I didn't have time to tell them we were coming," his mother said. "I hope that Papa isn't off in another village somewhere."

They walked down the road through narrow plots of corn, beans, and sunflowers. The sun was warm—not a cloud in the sky. The farmers were up early, weeding, hoeing, and checking the progress of the crops. The apple blossoms had faded, and the branches were budding with green and the promise of fruit. They passed one of the Revak cornfields.

"Look, Mama," Stefan said proudly, pointing to the field. "The corn will be taller than me by the time we get to July."

"You're doing well—learning that hard work pays off. Here's your proof," she said.

After walking an hour past Scheindorf, they came to a village built of whitewashed, mud-brick homes, the same as their village. The road ended at a church with two spires, one taller than the other. Mounds of colorful flowers, cornflowers and pink petunias, surrounded the church. Stefan could see the stones of a cemetery through the well-tended green shrubs and flowers.

"We turn left here," Gertrude said. "But let's get a drink of water from the pump. See if it's any better than our well." Gertrude primed the pump and worked the handle until water began to flow. It was cold and tasted wonderful to Stefan.

"Just as bad as our water," his mother said. "I miss the water of the city. Opa and Oma's water is much better. Just you wait."

Mother and son left the town, following the road through the lush green landscape of apple orchards and farmland. At the top of a hill, Stefan saw sunlight sparkle off a river not far away.

"Mama, look at the water across the meadow! Can we stop and soak our feet? Please?"

"Yes. I could use a rest too. We can stop and eat."

The beautiful riverbed, bordered by lacy white and tall yellow spikes of wildflowers, called to Stefan's aching feet. Oblivious to the pain, he ran through the meadow of flowers, swatting away the occasional bee, heading to the water. He sat down, rolled up his pants, took off his socks, and splashed in. The cool water felt so good!

"What is this river, Mama?"

Gertrude walked more slowly to the bank. "It's called the Someşul." She smiled for the first time that day. "In the spring, when the snow melts in the eastern mountains, the water fills the river, and it winds its way all the way through Mama and Papa's town and beyond into Hungary and the great River Tisza."

"Is the Tisza a big river, bigger than this one?"

"Yes, the Tisza is very wide and deep. It's so big that bridges have been built—in cities—in order to cross."

Stefan tried to imagine it and found he could not. "I hope someday I can see a bridge like that."

"Come out of the water. Sit with me. Let's eat."

Stefan walked out of the shallow water toward his

mother.

"Fresh bread and eggs sound good. I'm starving!"

"You're always hungry, my growing son." She smiled again and pulled out the food, wrapped in a scrap of cloth, from the rucksack. She put the cloth on the grassy knoll and placed the food on it. Stefan reached for an egg, peeled it, and ate it in two bites.

"Slow down," she said, grabbing his hand as he reached for another egg. "This is all we have until we get to Oma and Opa's."

"Okay," he said. "I'll slow down." He smiled at her, and she smiled back.

As they sat eating, he heard voices in the distance. They were singing in a language he did not understand.

"What's that, Mama?"

Stefan jumped up to see. Something was rumbling up the road. It was a house on wheels! Pulled by two dark horses, the light blue wagon had four windows. Each window had green shutters trimmed with yellow. Stefan had never seen anything like it.

"Look, Mama! Who are they?"

The singing got louder, and a second, then a third colorful house on wheels turned off the road into the meadow, heading to the river and directly toward them.

"They're coming this way!" Stefan said, excited to see the caravan more closely.

Gertrude stood up, took her son's hand, and whispered, "Roma! We must go."

"What are Roma?" Stefan asked. Fascinated, he watched the wagons rock and rattle toward them. His mother seemed concerned, but he could not see anything to fear. A matched pair of beautiful chestnut horses drew the wagons. The horses had a star of white between their huge brown eyes, and their long black manes were braided with flowers. Stefan, drawn to the horses, wanted to run and touch them. But he stayed back, concerned what his mother would say.

"Gypsies," she said under her breath. "They're a strange people. Some say they came from India a thousand year ago, and others swear they are Egyptians who hid baby Jesus from the Romans. They are untouchables. We must go!"

"Untouchables?"

"Get your shoes on—quickly!"

Stefan sat down, grabbed his socks, and struggled to put them on over his wet feet. All of a sudden, a pair of big, well-worn boots, covered with mud, stood near his toes. He looked up and stared into the face of the lead wagon's driver—a fierce-looking, rugged man. Now he understood why his mother seemed afraid. A tattered black hat shaded the man's face, and a wild red beard covered his face and trailed down the length of his shirt. His eyebrows were shaggy and dark. Long, disheveled dark hair hung to his shoulders, and his brown eyes, surrounded by deep creases, were fearless.

Stefan, spellbound by the spectacle, was speechless.

"Is this your river, boy?" the man's voice boomed in Romanian.

"No, sir."

"Then we don't need your permission to water the horses, do we?" said the woman behind him, still perched on the wagon seat. She laughed and swatted a fly with her blue hat. Her hair hung untamed and curly, black as coal. Her skirts were long and colorful, and she held a wooden pipe between her teeth. Her face was young but weathered by the sun.

The man and woman looked at each other and laughed again at their jokes. Their laughter startled a flock of ducks that had been feeding peacefully on the river. They squawked loudly and flew away.

"Stefan, get your shoes on—quickly!" Gertrude ordered.

Stefan snapped back into action. It was hard to pull his socks back onto his wet feet.

As Stefan wrestled with his shoes and socks, a boy leaped from the wagon's rear door and ran barefoot to him. The boy had black, curly hair and a crooked nose. He smiled and spoke to Stefan in a strange language, gesturing with his hands.

Stefan tried to understand him. *It's not Romanian—or Hungarian—or German.*

The friendly boy stuck out his hand, and Stefan took it. The boy pulled Stefan to his feet.

"We should go now," Gertrude said. "I can't understand them."

"It will be all right, Mama," Stefan said. He smiled at his new young friend, reached down, picked up the last hard-boiled egg, and passed it to the gypsy.

The young boy reached for the egg, peeled it quickly, and devoured it. He placed his hand on Stefan's shoulder and smiled. Then he walked over to the bearded lead driver and began talking, gesturing toward Stefan and his mother.

"What are they going to do to us?" Gertrude whispered to Stefan.

"Mama, I don't know," Stefan said. He reached out to take his mother's hand. It was freezing. She was still afraid, but he was not. The people spoke another language, lived in houses on wheels, and wore different clothes, but he was sure they meant no harm.

The wild-looking man walked over to Stefan and Gertrude. He towered over them. Speaking in Romanian he said, "Do you need a ride? We thank you for your kindness to Cappi. He hasn't had a fresh egg in weeks." The gypsy smiled and reached out his hand to Stefan. "I'm Lash. That's my wife, Macalla." Macalla waved a greeting from the wagon.

"It is good to meet you," Stefan replied politely, shaking the offered hand. His hand felt lost in the grip of Lash's hand. He glanced at his mother. She appeared puzzled and concerned by the interchange she did not understand. "It will be fine, Mama."

"We're going to Satu Mare. Are you headed that direction?" Stefan said.

"Yes, we can take you there, but we cannot enter the city. It is forbidden."

Stefan did not understand, but he thought better of asking why the caravan could not enter the city. He would ask his mother about it later.

"A ride would make the journey easier on my mother," Stefan said.

"It's settled then. An egg for a ride." Lash laughed. "We'll water the horses, wash up a bit, and be on our way."

Stefan found his way over to the horses. One of them looked at him with big brown intelligent eyes fringed with long lashes. He moved closer. She bumped her head into his chest, pushing him back, nearly knocking him off his feet. He stepped back.

"She's trying to tell you who's the boss," Lash said. "Just stand your ground. Let her smell your hand. Let her know you are a friend."

Stefan moved closer to the horse. She nuzzled him again. He reached out and let her smell his hand, then stroked her neck. Her shiny coat was soft and warm.

"She's beautiful," he said. Stefan felt an immediate bond.

"You might want to explain to your mother what's going on," Lash said, "before she faints."

He laughed again and climbed up on the wagon to lead the horses to the water.

"Can I help?" Stefan asked. He wanted to stay with the horses.

Lash smiled. "Come along then."

"Okay, Mama?" Stefan watched Gertrude raise her eyebrows.

"Get on with it," she said. She shook her head in submission and waved her hand for Stefan to go.

———••••———

Stefan and Gertrude said farewell to the Roma family in a field near the river, just outside the city of Satu Mare. The gypsies would make camp there for the night. The sun was beginning to set as they went on their way. Shadows lengthened, and a breeze picked up.

Stefan and Gertrude walked to the bridge over the Some ul. Though Gertrude's heart was still pounding from the journey, she marveled at the fact that these people had roamed the countryside for generations. All of their worldly possessions—and they were meager— were with them. She had never interacted with Roma before, but though she had been afraid at first, the time with them had changed something in her heart. She realized that they were people, just like the people in their village, who had chosen another way of life. Yet she was worried about what Stefan might say to her parents about their unusual ride. There was so much he did not understand.

As they walked, she listened to Stefan talk nonstop about the adventure: the wagon ride, the people, and the horses. She stopped at the end of the bridge and turned to Stefan. She put her hands on his shoulders, bent down, looked him in the eyes, and whispered, "Stefan, you must swear on everything holy that you will never tell anyone we rode in a gypsy wagon."

Stefan nodded somberly, though she could see the confusion in his eyes. "I swear, Mama."

"So that's the end of it, yes? Oh, my heart!" She pressed both hands over her heart. "I never thought I'd ever ride with gypsies."

Stefan was grinning. She gave him a playful swat on the arm. "Wipe that smile off your face. It's our secret, yes?"

"Yes, Mama," he said and stifled a laugh.

She shook her head in disapproval.

Just ahead, Satu Mare awaited them. For a few hours, Gertrude, distracted by the experience, had forgotten her sorrow and the reason for their visit to her parents. Entering the city, feelings of loss and worry—the sorrow of shattered dreams—flooded her thoughts. Tears misted her eyes, and she could barely see.

A horse-drawn wagon nearly hit them, and the scare brought her back to reality. The driver shouted at them to look out. She grabbed Stefan's hand and held him tight. The streets were busy with early evening traffic.

"Mama, look at all of those houses!" Stefan said over

the din of wagon wheels clattering over cobblestones. "I've never seen so many houses—and look at those black horses. Is that a carriage, Mama? Look at the lady with that big hat!"

Stefan peppered her with questions as they walked through the maze of streets, finally coming to her family home. They stood outside as she gathered her thoughts.

"Is this Opa and Oma's house? Were you born here?"

"Yes." She smiled.

Gertrude looked at the familiar tall green door flanked by pairs of windows, each window with an ornamental stone façade. Many of her village friends would consider the elegant two-story architecture a castle, but this was home. She was finally home—home where all her hopes and dreams had begun.

Gertrude turned to Stefan, straightened his shirt, and combed his hair with her fingers. "Papa's business is on the first floor, and we live on the second floor." She looked at his muddy shoes and shook her head. "Now be polite, say please and thank you, and don't eat them out of house and home."

He looked at her and nodded.

Gertrude took a deep breath. She turned the brass crank in the center of the door. A bell rang inside of the house.

Within minutes, the door opened, and her mother stood framed in the doorway. She was dressed in a white blouse embroidered with colorful cross-stitching and a long green skirt. A wide brown leather belt circled her ample waist. As always, her mother's hair and dress were perfect. Gertrude wondered how presentable she looked after a dusty day of travel. She wanted to run into her mother's arms, but she hesitated.

Her mother's mouth opened in surprise, and then a smile spread across her face. Gertrude's heart was racing. "Gertrude! We weren't expecting you! Come in! Come in!"

Gertrude flew into her mother's arms, finding the refuge and comfort she so desperately needed. Her guard down, she started to cry softly.

"What's wrong, Gertrude? Something must be to have you come so far without telling us."

Oma looked at Stefan. "My, you have grown! You look so much like your father—how is he, by the way?" She turned back to Gertrude.

"That's why we're here," she said.

Oma's smile turned into a look of concern. "Come in, come in. You must be tired and hungry. Your father is working at his desk. He will be happy to see you both."

———

Stefan lay dozing on a couch. His stomach was so full his pants were tight. The past few days had been fun—full of food and family. Oma spoiled him with sweet treats: marzipan candies in the shape of little fruits, cookies, chocolate, and apple strudel. His mother's family flooded the house day and night, and he had lost track of how many cousins he had met from the Erli side of the family. His Aunt Theresia came, and they shared news of Rosalia in America. It seemed like all they did was eat: potato pancakes, spätzle, Wiener Schnitzel, red cabbage, sauerbraten, and sausages. His mother was smiling again, and she seemed happy. Best of all, she hardly drank a drop, even though Stefan spotted schnapps in the house. The change in his mother made him feel better and worry less. The burden of his life had lifted for these few days, and it was wonderful and fun.

As he rested on the couch, he overheard his mother and Opa talking in his office. He kept his eyes closed and listened.

"The longer your husband can stay in American, the better odds that you and little Stefan will get there," Opa said. "I know it's hard on you, but you are strong, my daughter. You have a good head for figures and planning. You will get through this."

"Thank you, Papa," Gertrude said. "It is very hard. I am lonely and tired most of the time. Stefan works like a man. He's never had the chance to be a boy. He has no father—though Anton is in his life, and you."

"Hard work won't hurt him," Opa said. "Hard work will serve him well."

Stefan did not hear what his mother responded. He thought about what she had said. Was he not a boy? He supposed he wasn't—not like the other boys at school. He was more like a man, like his uncle and his mother told him. He felt proud of himself.

Opa continued, "While you are waiting for your husband, buy property. Property is a hard currency. Everyone wants and needs land. And American dollars will buy you more."

"Yes, Papa."

"Down the road, when you go to America—and you will—you can sell the land. Take the money with you to America. You'll need it there."

The next morning, Stefan and his mother left for Scheindorf. The basket they carried was heavy. Oma had sent them home with sausage, bread, cakes, and candies. His mother told him of her plans to buy land instead of selling it for now. She told him in a way that was firm and calm, not with tears and fear. He was relieved that his mother seemed so much better. She thought they could do good things with more land. He wondered how they would manage more land. He looked up at her as they walked and could see she was thinking, her face set in a focused, faraway look.

After six hours of walking from his grandparents' house, the basket was lighter since they had stopped for a quick meal. He wished the gypsies would come and pick them up again, as his feet ached. But he did not think his mother would like that.

About three kilometers from their village, his mother stopped and pointed.

"Stefan, who owns the field over there—the one gone to weeds?"

"That would be the old Hungarian man, Mama. The last I saw him, he and his son were here in the field. I haven't seen them for a long time."

"Do you know his name and where he lives?"

"I don't know his name," Stefan said. "But someone in the town might know. We can try the Hungarian village—it's not far."

"Let's go. I want to get the word out that we're buying, not selling land."

After a while, they entered the village. They headed toward the shop they saw and walked in. Stefan spoke to the shopkeeper in Hungarian, asking him who owned the neglected piece of land on the road to Scheindorf.

The shopkeeper smiled. "I believe you are talking about Németh Béla. He no longer farms. He owns a number of fields around our village, and all of them are without crops. He must be getting up there in age. Why are you interested in him?"

"We may have a buyer for his land," Stefan replied.

The merchant's brow furrowed. "He's a bit of a hermit, lives alone. Mind you, he doesn't get many visitors."

Stefan and his mother followed the directions of the shopkeeper. They found a dilapidated cottage in the midst of gnarled old trees, thistles that had grown three feet high and tall grasses. A narrow pathway led through the thick growth to the cottage porch.

"Be careful, Mama—these boards are rotting." Stefan took Gertrude's hand and guided her up the steps. They stepped on slippery green moss and mushrooms growing on the wet boards. "Are you sure we want to go in there, Mama?"

He looked up at his mother and saw her jaw set. He knew that look. She had made up her mind; she was not going to back down.

"I want his land. Knock on the door."

Stefan knocked hard, wondering what they might find.

A fit of coughing came from inside, startling Stefan. Then he heard a low, gravelly voice call out. Stefan could not make out the words. He turned to his mother, ready to run, but Gertrude took him by the hand and opened the door. The house was dark and the air still. Stefan smelled cigarette smoke, urine, garlic, and something rotting. He started to gag, and his eyes began to water.

Gertrude walked through the house searching for

the voice, and Stefan followed. Their path was a narrow walkway between piles of trash and puddles of rainwater from holes in the roof. In the back of the house, they found a man.

Németh Béla lay in bed, his face illuminated by the light that filtered through the flimsy, torn curtains. A cigarette hung from the corner of his mouth, and smoke filled the room. His face was deeply lined, his eyes sunken but bright even in the shadows. He was so thin, his bones showed through his skin. Stefan had never seen anyone so thin, or with skin so yellow. He wondered if this was what dying looked like.

The man was all alone.

"Why are you here?" he asked in Hungarian.

Stefan looked up at his mother for guidance.

Gertrude explained their search for land.

"You translate, Stefan," she said, pointing to the man.

Stefan explained in Hungarian.

The man looked at them a moment, and then he said, "Let me tell my story."

Mother and son looked at one another and nodded. There was nowhere to sit, so they stood as the old man relayed his history, punctuated by fits of coughing.

Béla's wife and their three sons were dead, the two oldest lost in the Great War. One died from influenza, buried in the German trench where he had died. The second son died in a bombing raid, his body rendered unrecognizable by the blast. Then their youngest son was digging a well when it collapsed, burying him, and two townspeople. Their bodies were never found. Soon after, Béla's wife, Katalin, took ill and passed.

Stefan could hardly imagine so much loss, but he

thought of how he missed his father, who was not even dead, and it made his heart hurt for this old, lonely man.

"So you see—I have no one." Béla coughed deeply and spit into a dirty rag. Using the smoldering stub of the cigarette, he lit another. "I don't believe I know you. Are you from the church?"

"Do you receive visitors from the church?" Gertrude asked.

"They come and take care of me."

"We're not from your church. We have come to buy your land."

At the mention of buying his land, the old man lifted himself up from the pillows on one elbow and grabbed Stefan's shirt with the other hand. In a quivering voice, he asked, "Are you the angels?"

His fear gone, Stefan leaned into the man. "Why do you think we are angels?"

"Because I prayed the angels would send someone to buy my land so I can give money to the church before I die."

Stefan did not think he or his mother was an angel. But before they left that house, they owned many new fields, and they had left Németh Béla just a little less lonely.

CHAPTER FOUR

"Take away love and our earth is a tomb."
Robert Browning

Scheindorf
Harvest 1923 to December 1924

"YOU'LL BE NINE this December. That makes you old enough to learn the art of making good German schnapps—the nectar of the gods." Anton laughed and continued to mash apples between oak paddles, collecting the juice and pulp in a large metal tub. Stefan watched him closely.

"The secret to delicious wine is quality fruit. Many people use the apples no one wants—but not us. Put quality in, Stefan, and you get quality out. Always remember that."

Anton and Stefan worked side-by-side crushing fruit in the two-year-old building behind Anton's house. Anton was serious about making spirits, and he now produced wine and stronger liquor made from pears, cherries, plums, and apples.

"Once we crush the apples, we'll let the fruit ferment."

Stefan paused to rest his arms and shoulders. The heady smell of concentrated apple wafted up from the tub. "How long will that take?"

"Keep pressing," Anton said. "Fermentation varies; we'll let this batch ferment for about three weeks. Then we'll distil the mash to get a high alcohol content." He stopped his running commentary on alcohol production, and a frown flitted across his face. "How is your mother getting along?"

"She has good days and bad days."

"She's been buying every plot of land she can get her hands on. First there was the old farmer near the Hungarian village who sold her something like thirty *kibbles?*"

"That was the day we came back from Oma and Opa's house—after we learned that we weren't going to America. We bought thirty-two."

"He died soon after, didn't he?"

"Yes—he thought we were angels when we came to see him."

Anton raised his dark eyebrows. "Angels, huh—that's interesting. How much land does Gertrude have now?"

"In America, it would be around sixty acres."

"So we are no longer speaking in kibbles." Anton laughed.

Stefan smiled. His mother liked to talk in terms of acres and dollars. He knew she was doing everything with the intention of going to America one day. Her dream had taken a blow, but it was far from dead.

"That must be tough to manage. Some are as much as two hours outside of town. I hear she bought a vineyard and some orchards. How many cows do you have now?"

"We have eight milkers, and they're doing fine," Stefan said. "We still have the two old browns we use for plowing."

Retrieving another basket, Anton placed peeled apples into the jaws of the masher.

"I got a letter from your father this week," he said after a moment.

Stefan stopped working. He did not expect that.

"Papa? What did he say?"

"He was concerned. He heard from your Uncle Johan that you've had at least three hired hands, and for one reason or another, they've all quit, the last one after only two months. Is that true?"

"That's true," Stefan said quietly. Worry and exhaustion percolated up. His jaw tightened. He would not let Anton see his feelings this time. His mother's impatience, fueled by drink, had led to her firing each of the men, one by one. No one could survive her expectations or her tongue.

Stefan continued to work. He would say nothing more.

Anton nodded. "Your father asked me to work for your mama while he's in New Jersey. He thinks it would help. What do you think?"

Hope sparked through Stefan. He looked up at his uncle and fought back tears of gratitude. Uncle Anton help them? Would he step in as the man of the farm? Stefan would have more time with him. They would share the burden as a family.

"Would that be all right? Do you think your mother will accept my help?"

Stefan wrestled with his thoughts. He wanted his uncle to come and help them more than anything, but he did not think Mama would like it. Anton would stand up to her.

Anton continued, "What would you think if I worked with you for a while, maybe for a year, starting with the corn harvest, and planting the wheat this fall and through the winter, next spring, and summer. Hopefully, your papa will be home after that."

Stefan bowed his head. "Mama is not good at asking for help. She thinks we can do it on our own." Then he looked Anton in the eyes. "Asking for help is a sign of weakness."

"Asking for help is not a sign of weakness. It means you are taking responsibility for getting the work done." Anton paused. "Do you need my help?"

Stefan flung his arms around his uncle and buried his head in his shoulder. He smelled apple and soap. His heart spilled over with love. Stefan longed for his father, for someone to sometimes step between him and his mother, for someone to lean on every once in a while. He felt so alone.

Anton tightened his arms around Stefan and held on. They said not a word.

⸻

It took perseverance and several conversations for Stefan to convince his mother that they needed Anton's help—especially during the fall. They had to harvest crops before they began to rot, scavengers and birds ate them, or the snow came and made fieldwork impossible. Each crop had a cycle, from the corn to the sunflowers to the potatoes. He was grateful for his uncle's help and companionship. Anton was a great teacher and a hard worker, but the burden of the work still fell on Stefan's shoulders.

Always hungry, Stefan was heading from the barn to the house for something to eat one October afternoon when he heard voices shouting in anger.

"Gertrude, you are my brother's wife, but that does not give you the right to talk to me that way!"

"I'll talk to you any way I want!" Gertrude screamed, her voice slurred.

Stefan's heart sank. She had been drinking again.

Shrill and angry, she yelled, "You work for me. I pay you!"

Uncle Anton's voice boomed. "Gertrude, you're drunk—and you didn't get it from us. I told my wife not to sell to you. You're not the Gertrude my brother married—the girl I remember—when you drink."

"Who are you to tell me when to drink or when not to drink? You have no idea what I put up with!"

"Gertrude, calm down—put that down!"

Stefan, his heart pounding, ran toward the house, a shovel still in his hand. What was happening? Was his mother going to hurt Uncle Anton?

His mother's voice cut through the air. "Get out of my house and off my land! You're fired!"

What was she thinking? This could not be happening.

"It's too late for that, because I quit!"

Stefan finally reached the house. He nearly ran into his uncle. Anton's face was flushed with anger.

Anton stopped before Stefan. He shook his head. He was breathing hard. "I'm sorry, Stefan, but I can't work for your mother anymore. I've had enough."

He turned and walked away.

Gertrude appeared at the door. "What are you looking at?" she snapped. Her eyes were dark with rage.

Frozen in place, Stefan felt as if he could not breathe.

"Give me that," she ordered. She reached out and grabbed the shovel from his hand, then raised it to strike him. "I'll teach you some manners!"

Stefan ducked, shielding his head with his hands. Out of the corner of his eye, he saw a hand reach out. Uncle Anton twisted the shovel out of his mother's hands and stood between them.

"Touch that boy again, and that'll be the last thing you remember!"

Gertrude looked stunned. No one moved.

Anton paused and said more quietly, "Now go inside and sober up."

Gertrude's head dropped, and Stefan thought he saw her eyes fill with tears. She turned around and went into the house.

Anton passed the shovel to Stefan. "Let's get to work."

His heart pounding and his eyes burning with tears, Stefan finally found his voice.

"You're not quitting?"

"Not today." Anton put his arm around Stefan's shoulders, and they walked back to the barn.

———•——

The weeks turned into months. Together they dug the furrows and planted seed potatoes, the tubers a little larger than a walnut. Winter passed quickly into spring, and once again, it was time to plant corn, then sunflowers.

The work was hard, but it was easy to see the fruit of their labor. Uncle and nephew took pleasure in the growing season, watching seeds sprout, walking through the corn checking for rot and disease, harvesting sunflower seeds, and making oil—the continuous cycle of life.

It was dusk in late spring; the long day was ending. Stefan walked with Anton toward the shed. Both were tired, quiet with their own thoughts. Stefan dreaded going home to his mother. He never knew what to expect. The resolute spirit and hope she had shown after visiting her parents had dissipated as the new land brought more responsibilities and work. He could feel the rising undercurrent of her rage. She continued to drink, and though she had come close to striking him, she had not. It was an uneasy truce. He did not understand her need to drink. He guessed it helped numb her feelings of loss.

Before they could reach the shed, Gertrude emerged from the shadows. She held a razor-sharp mowing scythe over her head. Her eyes smoldered with anger.

"Where is it?" she demanded.

Stefan's heart pounded. She looked ready to swing the scythe at them both. What could have happened?

"Mama, don't!" He stepped back and grabbed Anton, pulling him away.

Anton stepped around Stefan, stood in front of him, and said in a calm voice, "Gertrude, put that down. What are you talking about?"

"You know what I'm talking about!" She screamed, "The money!"

"The money?"

"Don't act innocent, you thief! You found the purse and stole it from the house!"

Gertrude lunged at Anton, swinging the scythe in an arc toward his head. Anton sidestepped the blow. Stefan froze in his tracks. Anton pushed him away, and they both ran behind a nearby cart. Gertrude wobbled on her feet, still wielding the dangerous scythe.

Beside him, Anton trembled with anger. "No one calls me a thief," he said. "I promised my brother, but a promise only goes so far. I'm through!"

"You're fired!" she said.

Gertrude dropped the scythe, and wove her way back to the house, unsteady on her feet.

Stefan could hardly believe what had just happened. He was breathing hard. Surely, this would be like last time—Uncle Anton would not really go. His mother's decision could not be final, even if she had tried to kill her brother-in-law a moment ago.

And yet he knew the truth—her drunken rage might have ruined everything in a moment.

His heart told him that this time it had.

Anton turned to him and said, "Come stay with us for a while."

The impact of what had happened finally hit Stefan with a great sense of loss. His eyes filled with tears. He took a deep breath.

"Thank you, Uncle, but I belong with my mother."

That evening, while Gertrude slept in a drunken stupor, Stefan searched the house. He found the purse of coins where she had hidden it—inside an empty kitchen crock.

The next morning, Gertrude joined Stefan at the table. She was exhausted, her throat parched, and her head throbbed. Her memories of the day before were dim, but she knew she had lost a bag of money—that Anton had stolen it. Had she confronted him about it? She thought she had. She hoped so.

There was a pitcher of fresh milk on the table. Next to the pitcher was the missing leather bag of coins. She felt her heart beat in her throat.

Where had that it come from? Had Anton brought it back? Stefan? Her thoughts were black and venomous. She trusted no one.

"Where did you get that? Did he give it to you?"

She snatched the bag, spilled the contents on the table, and began to count the money. The money represented years of saving. It would pave their way to a better life in America. It was her escape from this life. She had saved everything she could. She desperately needed this money. Her dream depended on it.

She watched Stefan sip his milk. He put his cup down and looked at her with dark eyes that betrayed his anger and disappointment.

"I found it right where you hid it, Mama. Uncle Anton had nothing to do with this." Stefan took another sip of milk and pushed the cup away. "Do you remember what you did last night?"

Gertrude stared at her son. She felt like her head would explode. She searched her memory for what had happened. She remembered stumbling through the house, trying to find her stash of coins, frustrated, then furious.

"I remember that I couldn't find the money. The only person in the house—besides you—was Anton. He must have taken the money. I went to find you." Gertrude sighed, put her head down, and put her hands over her eyes. "I don't remember."

"You tried to kill him."

Gertrude shook her head. Had she? Could she have done such a thing? Rage boiled through her. She was angry with everyone—her husband, off in America; his brother, probably talking about her to his wife. Life was too hard. She had no hope of anything changing. Her heart pulsed with sadness and a deep sense of loss.

Bitter words spilled out. "Someday, when you marry, promise me you won't leave your wife and go away for years and years."

Stefan was quiet. Was he listening? She reached over, grabbed his arm, and squeezed it hard. "Do you hear? Do you understand what I am saying?"

"Mama, that hurts!" He pulled away from her.

She grabbed his hand, locking it between both of hers, and looked in his eyes. She saw fear. She had never wanted to see fear there. It broke her heart. Yet she could not stop.

"Do you hear me?" she pleaded in desperation. He had to understand her pain. "Promise me you will never leave your wife—to suffer alone."

She stopped to swallow and looked down in embarrassment. Quietly, she said to herself, "Look what I've become."

His voice was low. "I promise, Mama."

Gertrude took a few breaths to compose her thoughts. She looked straight ahead and spoke to the room. "My husband is dead to me. I am a widow, or I may as well be."

Her words hung in the silence. She let him go and sat back in her chair. Her eyes found her son's eyes.

"You're too young to understand. When you are alone, when the man you love is gone, there is an emptiness nothing can fill. I don't know if he loves me anymore. I can't feel it."

She looked down at her empty hands. Her heart was breaking. She had no hope.

"Mama." She felt Stefan reach over and tug her sleeve. She looked at him.

"Mama, what are we to do? I can't do it myself. I work before and after school, and there is still not enough time to get everything done, and after the school term, we'll need to bring in the wheat. I can't get it to the thresher myself. We need Uncle Anton."

Gertrude listened and thought for a moment before speaking.

"We don't need Uncle Anton," she said, straightening her shoulders. She stood up from the table and picked up the purse. "Go see Herr Keller. He has horses and a good wagon you can use to haul wheat to the thresher."

———◆———

After school that day, Stefan went in search of Fritz Keller and his three sons, Anton, Josef, and Adolf, who were working a tract of land south of the village. Their two horses grazed in the meadow in the shade near the weathered old hay wagon. Singing rose from the field. He walked over to the wagon and picked up a scythe. He followed the voices and found the Kellers mowing hay, swinging their scythes in a rhythm together while singing the German folk song *"Du, du liegst mir im Herzen."* Smiling, Stefan sang with them, joining in their work.

Later, they all stopped for a water break. While they were sitting in the shade, Stefan decided it was time to ask for help.

"Perhaps we could make a trade. Some of our sunflower oil or corn for your wagon and the team? My mother and I could really use the help to harvest our crop."

Herr Keller's smile faded. "You seem to be a fine lad, Stefan, but, if you need help, go to your mother," Herr Keller said. "She has no problem drinking, and if she put as much effort into working as she does the bottle, you would have all the help you need. Our horses and wagon will not be used to enable your mother's weakness for drink."

Stefan swallowed hard as embarrassment flooded him. Despair quickly followed. He had no help to bring in the wheat.

He got up, thanked the Kellers for the water, and headed back home to get in some of the crops that afternoon. He had plenty of time to think as he walked the distance back home, got the wagon from the barn, and gathered his scythe and a jug of water.

In the field, he began to mow, swinging the scythe rhythmically, back and forth. The work was calming. The weather was clear and warm.

What was the song the Kellers sang to pass the time?

Stefan remembered and began to sing with his work. It made him feel better. Wrapped up in the music, focused on the chore, dust flying in the sunlight of late afternoon, he thought he heard a woman singing.

He turned. Gertrude stood behind him. They both stopped singing. He gave his mother a tentative smile.

She smiled back.

Gertrude took a scythe from the wagon, began swinging the blade, and started again to sing. His heart felt a little lighter as they worked together.

Some weeks later, Stefan was pushing a cart loaded with corn. The road was so full of ruts and mud that it was a constant battle to keep the wagon steady and the corn in the wagon. One of the wheels became wedged in a rut. Stefan pushed, and the cart tilted and overturned, spilling corn all over the road. Frustrated and tired, he attempted to right the cart. No matter how he pulled or pushed, the wheel was wedged. He leaned over the cart to rest.

"Need some help?" He heard a familiar voice, and his heart soared with hope. He turned around to see Uncle Anton. They had not seen one another since the confrontation at the farm.

"Yes," he sighed in frustration. "I could really use some help. I can't seem to get the cart out of the rut, and every time I push, more corn ends up in the mud."

"Let's try it together."

They righted the cart, then pushed and pulled together, and the cart started to move again. Stefan and Anton picked up all the corn and piled it in the cart.

"Thank you," Stefan said and passed Anton a jug of water.

Anton took a long swallow and wiped his face with his kerchief.

"Is your mother picking corn with you?"

Embarrassed, Stefan did not know what to say. She had helped him for a little while but soon dropped off again, leaving him to carry the load himself. He loved his mother and did not want to dishonor her. But Anton's direct question did not give him much room to excuse her actions.

Anton walked over and put a hand on Stefan's shoulder. "You can tell me, Stefan."

"She's drinking more. I'm worried about her. She drinks herself to sleep, then sleeps most of the day." Stefan stopped. "I really shouldn't be talking about it. It's hard enough to live in the village—people knowing how she drinks—judging us."

"Have you heard from your father?"

"No, Papa has not written for some time."

Anton looked at Stefan and gave him an understanding smile. "You need your father. Your mother needs her husband."

Stefan nodded. His heart ached.

"I will write him and tell him to come home," Anton said. "He's been away too long. He needs to come home and take care of his family."

Stefan nodded and looked down. He had never even considered this solution. Would it mean giving up his mother's dreams? How would she react? She had become so unpredictable. He thought some more. Yet it was right. It was what they needed. He had one selfish hope. Maybe if his father were home, he could go on to school— become more than a farmer. With his father home that might be possible.

"Stefan," his uncle said, interrupting his thoughts. "You know I did not steal that money from your mother."

"I know—I found the money where she hid it. She

knows it too."

"Let's get this load home," Anton said with an encouraging smile.

"Thank you," Stefan said as he approached the cart.
"Yes, we need Papa—but I could never have done any of
this without you."

———•+•———

Two weeks before Christmas, Gertrude sat at the
kitchen table and looked out the window at the snow
that was drifting down in huge flakes. She picked up her
hot mug of soup. It was comforting to hold in her tired
and cold hands. She inhaled the fragrance and took a
small sip. The broth soothed her.

She put the mug down by the envelope on the table.
She stared at it for a long time. She reached out and
touched it, running her fingers slowly across the familiar
handwriting, the postmarks from America. What would
he say? Her hands trembled as she opened it. She pulled
out a single sheet of paper, read it, put her head on the
table, and wept.

A door opened and shut—Stefan was coming into
the house. She quickly dried her eyes on her apron as
her son appeared in the kitchen door.

"Mama, what's wrong?"

She patted the kitchen table with her hand. "Come
and sit."

Stefan sat down. She saw the worry in his eyes. He
was so young, she realized—so young to be so weary, so
burdened.

She almost hated to admit it, but the letter had

brought her hope for the first time in years. It was not the path she would have chosen, but things would change at last.

She reached across the table and grasped his cold hand. "Your father is coming home," she said. "He is booked on the SS *Stuttgart*, sailing from New York."

She watched her son's face light up—the young man looked like a boy again.

"When, Mama?"

She picked up the letter. "He leaves on January 30. He will travel to Bremerhaven, Germany, by way of Plymouth and Cherbourg."

She put the letter down on the table.

"He should be here in late February."

Stefan got up and wrapped his arms around her. "Merry Christmas, Mama."

Gertrude started to cry.

CHAPTER FIVE

"If you love somebody, let them go, for if they return,
They were always yours.
If they don't, they never were."
Kahlil Gibran

Scheindorf
February 1925

GERTRUDE CLUTCHED THE wool shawl tightly around
her shoulders as she knelt before the statue of St.
Anthony, finishing her novena—praying for the safe
travel of her husband. The votive candles flickered in
the drafty house. The wood floor was cold, and the chill
crept into her body, invading her bones.

She shivered. *Will he come home today? Will he still
love me—the old woman that I have become? Will he still
want me?* She pushed away thoughts of her drinking, of
her anger. It would all change if he loved her. He had
been gone four years.

She sighed, brought her rosary to her lips, made the
sign of the cross, and stood.

The news of her husband's coming home had given
her purpose. The house was spotless, the glass polished,

the root cellar full of onions, potatoes, garlic, apples, and turnips. She had made strudel, cakes, and bread, stockpiling enough food to feed an army. She had decided which chicken would be his first dinner, and her spice boxes were full of the summer's dried herbs.

Gertrude added more wood to the kitchen stove and rubbed her hands together to warm them. The stove's heat filled the room, and she could finally feel the tips of her fingers. She picked up her large knife and started chopping vegetables for a hearty soup while she waited for her son to return from a village store. The pot of water steamed on the stove, and she added the vegetables. Then she took dried thyme and basil, crushed them between her fingers, and inhaled. The scent took her back to the warm days of summer, and she smiled.

The door to the house opened, and cold air rushed in.

"Stefan, quick, close the door! It's freezing!"

She quickly sprinkled the herbs into the soup and gave it a quick stir with her wooden spoon. Wiping her hands on her apron, she walked in the direction of the cold air.

Her heart pounded. Tears filled her eyes.

"Do you remember me?" said the tall, handsome man who stood in her doorway. He was dressed in a dark, long wool coat, and he spoke in a voice she knew as well as her own. He put two large suitcases down on the floor.

"Mama, look who I found!"

Young Stefan ran from behind his father, carrying the sugar and spices. When she saw her son beaming, she started to smile. It was real. He was home.

Gertrude could not help herself. She began to cry.

Her husband came toward her, arms outstretched. She walked into his arms, felt the fine wool of his coat and the warmth of his body. She nestled her face in his neck and smelled his familiar scent, and she finally went weak. The separation was over. Her husband, her rock, had returned.

She could feel her son's arms wrapped around the both of them—a family together again. No one said anything for a long time.

Suddenly, she wondered aloud, "How do I look?" Embarrassed, she pulled away from her two men. Her hand flew up to her head, mindlessly arranging her hair.

Her husband started to laugh. "You look wonderful."

"You know me too well."

He nodded, and their eyes met. She felt shy. Who had he become—this husband of her youth? She would wait, and they would talk privately tonight, in their bed together after many years of being alone.

"Mama, I got everything you asked for." Stefan broke the silence and rushed past them to the kitchen. "I'm starving!"

"Don't you want to see what I've brought you from America? Or would you rather eat?"

Gertrude laughed. "Why don't I feed you both, and then we'll open gifts, okay?" Smiling, she felt peaceful, complete. Everything in this moment was perfect. She did not want it to end.

—————⋅◆⋅—————

Stefan, hungry from his journey, ate two bowls of his wife's fragrant vegetable soup. He could not get enough of the comfort that warmed him to the core. Her bread was as he remembered it: hearty and rich. He sipped his hot coffee, laced with creamy butter, just the way he liked it. He was home. His heart was as full as his stomach. He sat relaxed at the kitchen table, enjoying the nonstop chatter of his son, not really listening, just taking it all in. It had been a long and tiring trip back. America had made him a different man, and yet, he was the same. This place was the same. It felt good and right to be home.

He watched Gertrude move about the kitchen, clearing plates and food, bringing more. She smiled and rarely spoke—but then there was no room for conversation as his son filled up the space between them with his stories and news.

Anton had written of his Gertrude's drinking—of her sorrow, of her rage, and of how she took out her anger on their son. He did not know how he would reach her, but perhaps with time and love, she would be the woman he knew she could be. He knew what it was like to be lonely. He understood frustration and hard work. He felt her suffering and ached with guilt that he had put her through it. The separation was a sacrifice they had agreed to make, but it had not worked as they planned. From now on, they would work hard together, not alone.

He smiled. This would not all change in a day. Gertrude looked over at him and smiled in return. In one glance, his heart connected with hers.

It was finally time for gifts. He pushed his chair back from the table and walked to his suitcases. He opened one and searched through the clothes until he found a box wrapped in blue tissue paper.

"This is for you, my lovely wife. You deserve more, but this was all I could bring. I hope you like it."

Gertrude reached for the gift and gently held it in her hands.

"Open it, Mama!" Stefan jumped up and hovered close to his mother.

She smiled and carefully removed the delicate paper. Stefan watched her obvious joy as she looked at the white enamel box and opened the ornate brass clasp. She reached inside of the red silk-lined box and took out a delicate, sterling silver hand mirror with a pink rose inlaid on the back. Gertrude looked at herself in the mirror.

"Still the face of the most beautiful girl in the world."

He watched her blush, her eyes downcast. He meant what he said. She was beautiful, so beautiful, to him.

"As for you, my son, something I hope you will treasure for many years." Stefan picked up a large black leather case with brass corners. "Your mother told me that you have a strong voice and a talent for music— like your mother. Every singer needs a musical instrument. Come over here and help me open it."

Together, father and son opened the latches on the hinged case. The case, lined in red velvet, held what looked to be a small organ, with ivory and ebony keys. The instrument, decorated with inlaid mother-of-pearl and colorful wood, was a beautiful work of art. Stefan watched his son's eyes grow wide.

"It's an accordion."

"What does it do?"

"You use the keys to play—like an organ—and it can sound like many instruments, depending on how you push the buttons. See, let me show you."

Stefan picked up the accordion and squeezed the bellows while playing a few keys. The sound that came out was loud and less than melodic.

"I'm no accordion player," he laughed. "I did some work for a friend. His name is Candido Iorio, and he made it for us. He came to America from Italy and started making accordions and selling them in 1907. It's a fine instrument."

He watched his son gently run a finger over the keys. "Papa, thank you! It is beautiful—look at the wood, Mama! I can't wait to learn to play it."

"America has people from all over the world who come to make a better life for themselves and their families. I want us to go back to America." Stefan looked up at Gertrude. "We'll go back, one day, as a family. What do you think?"

He saw her smiling eyes fill with tears of hope.

She nodded. "Yes, we must go back. Together."

PART II

CHAPTER SIX

"Without ambition one starts nothing.
Without work one finishes nothing.
The prize will not be sent to you. You have to win it."
Ralph Waldo Emerson

Scheindorf, Romania/Hungary
1925–1931

WHEN STEFAN REVAK returned from the United
States in 1925, some things had changed, but many were
the same. Scheindorf had suffered a terrible drought in
1924 and was still recovering. Wheat supplies were low.
Though borders would change over the years, Scheindorf
was located in democratic Romania. The country had
some seventy-one counties, 498 rural districts, and 8,879
communities.

Stefan was intelligent and well-liked. He knew everyone in Scheindorf and for miles in every direction. He
was popular, he spoke well, and he was not shy. His
plans did not include spending the rest of his life farming.
He would keep the farm but hire others to work it. With
a head for business, a way with people, and ambition, he
was a born politician.

Over time, Scheindorf needed a new mayor. Stefan, respected and admired by the community for his world experience and leadership, was elected to serve. He became the mayor, called a "judge," at age thirty-six.

Stefan found himself busier than he ever imagined. While he was in America, Gertrude had purchased a share in the local gristmill. He was one of six shareholders and became the mill's manager. Considering how the mill could serve the community as well as its owners, he developed a system where the mill would grind flour free if the farmers gave a portion of their flour. The grain farmers were happy, and the mill owners sold the flour, making a profit.

In his role as mayor, Stefan mediated disputes and worked to develop the community, including the school. The school had expanded to over one hundred students. He added a new teacher, Margarita Lang, with impressive credentials. Frau Lang taught the older students, and for the first time, the primary school offered the seventh year of education.

The demand for Uncle Anton's fine schnapps, wines, and fruit elixirs was great. The two brothers, as well as other investors, opened a large *schnapps haus* and created a community wine cellar in a cave for storing wine by the barrel. Scheindorf was thriving. People came from all around to make their whiskey at the Revaks' schnapps haus. As they were at the center of an agricultural region, it was logical to make whiskey with one's leftover crops: potatoes, corn, wheat, and rye. The Revaks received payment in whiskey. If a farmer made ten liters, one liter went to them.

Fourteen-year-old Stefan woke up early on a Saturday morning in late spring. He lay in bed for a few minutes thinking. Over the years since his father had returned from America, Stefan continued to spend the bulk on his time managing the farm. His father was too busy to offer much help. Stefan had swallowed his disappointment about not being able to continue his education outside of Scheindorf. He had hoped that when his father returned, he would join him in work on the farm and he could continue school. Stefan's hopes and dreams of being more than a farmer would have to wait.

But today was different—a new adventure!

He threw off his covers and got out of bed. He had morning chores to do before they could leave for Satu Mare. They were going to the spring auction to buy horses. They would travel with one of his father's investors, Wendelin Koch.

Stefan bolted out of the house and looked across the road. He saw one of the Ditzig girls run down the road toward the home of Frau Leili, her grandmother. What was her name? Maria? How old was she now? Six? She was pretty, he thought, for a little girl. The blue ribbons in her dark hair streamed behind her as she ran. Maria saw him across the road and gave him a cheerful wave. Then she ran up the stairs to her grandmother's brightly painted red door. Her mother must be working in the fields today. He smiled and went to the barn.

When he returned from his chores, Stefan's father was at the table eating breakfast, and his mother was packing food for their journey.

"Sit, sit," his mother said. "Eat. You'd best get there early. You have much to do."

Stefan sat down at the table. His mother set down a

brown glazed pottery bowl of warm oatmeal, sprinkled with plump, dark raisins and a spoonful of melted butter. He leaned down and inhaled.

"Smells great, Mama," he said. He added some fresh warm milk, gave the cereal a stir, and ate like a starving man.

Between bites, he looked up. "Mama, are these the raisins we dried from last summer?"

His mother nodded and smiled.

Within minutes, Stefan wolfed down his food and got up from the table.

"I packed some food for Herr Koch since he is so kind to take you along with him." Gertrude shook a finger at Stefan in warning. "Remember to share, my son. Be sure to offer him food first."

"Yes, Mama!"

Stefan could not remember when he was more excited. He had heard about the horse auction from his father. It was the first time he had been included in such a trip. It made him feel grown up and important to go with his father and a business partner.

Stefan and his father met Herr Koch with his team and wagon in the village and traveled the winding road through the fields and forests to Satu Mare. While his father and Herr Koch talked about crops, investments, and community issues, Stefan listened and learned.

The time passed quickly, and soon they were on the east side of the city. The rail yard was bustling with people and chugging locomotives. Shrill whistles warned of the trains' approach and departure, while the engines spewed dark coal smoke and soot so thick it dusted Stefan's clean white shirt with black pollen. Herr Koch navigated through the busy city, finally stopped at the city's **Grădina Romei**. Stefan wondered why it was called a garden. It was mostly an open area of brown dirt, rocks, and a few shrubs. There was a muddy pond in the center.

"This park, the Rome Garden, was once a beautiful place," explained Herr Koch to Stefan. "But during the Great War, we could not keep it up anymore. The lake used to be clear blue and stocked with fish—now as you can see it is brown and covered with slime."

Stefan listened halfheartedly, his eyes locked on the moving landscape of thousands of horses that filled the space, horses of every breed imaginable—stomping, pawing the ground, rearing up in defiance. Breeders held on tight to ropes, herding horses of all shapes, sizes, and colors into corrals; and buyers walked through the churning mass searching for the right match. The scene was loud, with men shouting over the chaos and horses stomping, snorting, and neighing. The smells of hay, manure, and sweat drifted on the wind along with clouds of swirling brown dust.

Stefan and his father got off the wagon and thanked Herr Koch for the ride. Herr Koch tilted his hat in farewell and drove the team away.

Enthralled by the spectacle, Stefan followed his father, almost losing sight of him as the judge wove his way through the throngs of people and horses. Stefan heard a whinny and turned to see a pair of gray foals standing by their parents, a great stallion and mare, both with wide backs and muscular, thick legs. The stallion stood what seemed to be nearly sixteen hands tall.

"Pop, come look!" Stefan called and reached out to pull his father closer to the horses.

Speaking in German, the seller explained that the

breed, called *Pinkafo* or *Pinkafield,* produced gentle, hard-working, and powerful horses. He pointed out the muscular neck and chest, powerful hefty legs, and thick mane and tail of the breed.

Stefan thought the gray horses were wonderful. He had never seen a family of horses. They should have a whole family, he thought—to raise, to ride, and to work on the farm.

One of the foals walked toward him tentatively, nudging him, smelling him. Stefan had come prepared. He reached out to stroke her between the eyes and down to the nose. He pulled out a small apple from his pocket and reached out to her with his open hand. The roughness of her pink tongue tickled his hand as she scooped it into her mouth and ate it in one bite. The other foal was curious and quickly came over too. He pulled out another apple and held it out, and the foal nibbled at his hand and picked up the apple. He had instantly made friends.

"For hauling, pulling a plow, or any kind of fieldwork, you can't go wrong with these animals. I have been raising them for years. They are calm, intelligent creatures. You won't be disappointed." The seller waited while the judge considered. Stefan looked eagerly to his father.

"They are impressive indeed. But we just got started— we need to go to the auction first, then we'll see." The judge shook the breeder's hand and walked away. Stefan was disappointed. He had already fallen in love with the family.

When they had walked a few steps away from the breeder, Stefan Senior turned to his son and said, "Best not to settle on the first thing you see. This is a big investment—and we'll have to live with it for a long time." He smiled and put his hand on his son's shoulder. "But that was a good start."

Stefan smiled at his father and let the advice sink in. He would go along with his father, but he still wanted those horses. He knew that he would be their primary caretaker—that they would work with him. He would remind his father about them after they looked at others. He was not ready to give up.

They walked to the busy auction corral. Buyers stood, some leaning in, others sitting on the rails of the wooden fence that ringed the corral. Everyone jostled for a position to see the merchandise. Stefan could feel the intensity of concentration and competition in the air.

The auctioneer stood on a raised, covered platform, and as a horse came into the arena, the auctioneer began a rapid-fire sales pitch. The selling took place at lightning speed. It made Stefan's head spin. He could hardly follow one sale, and then another quickly followed.

Stefan watched his father survey the scene.

"It's moving too fast for me," the judge said. "Let's go back and take a look at those grays again. What do you think?" He smiled at Stefan. "I needed more time to make a decision."

"I understand, Papa. I felt good about the grays. They seemed right for what we need."

Stefan tried to calm his enthusiasm. He did not want to seem too eager.

They started to walk back to where they saw the Pinkafo. Stefan's father put his arm around his son's shoulders. "Since you will be doing most of the work with them, it seems right that you should have a say in this decision. So think carefully, Stefan. You take a look at the horses, and I'll talk with the breeder."

Stefan nodded and swallowed hard, suddenly feeling the burden of responsibility.

When they reached the breeder, Stefan's father said, "Stefan, take a good look at the horses. Make sure they are healthy—that there is nothing wrong with them."

"Sure, Papa—I'll do my best."

A little anxious about his ability, he remembered watching Uncle Anton look at a horse before he bought it. As Stefan started to examine the horses as best he knew, he could hear his father negotiating in German with the breeder. He walked each of the horses around to make sure they weren't lame. He checked their hooves for cracks and deformities. He tried hard to check the color of their mouths and the condition of their teeth, but the foals were not very cooperative. He looked at the lines of their backs for any deformities.

Stefan overheard his father say, "If we think the horses are right for us, we'll take all four. We will keep the family together. Does that sound good?"

Stefan's heart started to race. This was a big decision—a huge investment. These would be his very first horses, and he would have to live with this decision for a long time.

"And since we would be saving you the commission from the auction, we expect that you will give us a fair price for the team. Yes?"

Stefan paused for a moment to watch the breeder while his father sweetened the final offer. "And an even better price—because I can pay you in United States dollars."

The breeder smiled and nodded.

"What do you think of that?" His father smiled.

The judge turned to his son without waiting for an

answer. "So, Stefan, before I finalize this deal, what do you think?"

Stefan walked over.

"Well, Papa, they look good to me. I looked them over as best as I could. I have a good feeling about them."

The breeder continued to smile. The two men discussed the price, agreed on it, and shook hands.

The breeder turned and reached out his hand to shake Stefan's young hand. "Congratulations, son. You bought yourself four wonderful animals."

Stefan smiled, and his chest swelled with pride. They had made a deal together—Stefan and his father.

"Thank you, sir," he said, shaking the man's hand with enthusiasm.

"What's next, Stefan?" his father asked.

Feeling very grown up, Stefan smiled and said, "Well, Papa, now we need a wagon."

His father and the breeder both laughed.

"You might try the shop on Traian Boulevard," the breeder said. "A Hungarian owns it. He knows his craft. They will be open today because of the auction. Tell Gerhard I sent you."

———————

Stefan led the grays into the large wooden barn that was the wainwright's workshop. While the big horses waited patiently, he spoke in soothing tones to the foals, both skittish in the unknown enclosure. The mare nickered and nudged one foal closer to her.

Gerhard, the wagon builder, walked in and shook

both of their hands. He wore a once-white shirt, now gray, with a full-length brown leather apron. His shaggy beard and brown hair were peppered with sawdust and wood chips, telltale clues to his craft. Stefan's father and Gerhard left Stefan with the horses and walked into the attached shed where three completed wagons were ready to sell.

Stefan turned his back to the horses and peered out toward the wagons on display as the wainwright explained the features of each. He liked the large wagon, brightly painted dark red with yellow trim. It had smaller wheels on the front—they would make it easier to turn. He waited while his father considered the choices.

Life had changed so much since his father had come home. He was not alone anymore. He was learning from his father and being included in outings like today, even allowed to help make decisions. It felt so right.

"What do you think, Stefan?" His father spoke from the shed.

"The one with the smaller wheels—they will make it easier to turn, Papa."

"Good choice—mine exactly!"

Stefan was pleased that his father and he agreed.

"Come, bring the horses." Gerhard motioned to Stefan. "We'll get them measured and harnessed."

Within minutes, the two mature horses were harnessed with identical leather collars and traces, bridles and reins measured and fitted. Soon they were ready to go. Stefan tied the two foals to the back of the wagon and climbed up into the seat next to his father.

His father handed him the reins. "Let's go," he said.

"Papa, I don't know how." Stefan looked at his father with concern.

The judge smiled. "Son, there is no better time than now. I'm with you—it is good practice, and you'll learn from your mistakes. You can do it. Just take them slow until you get the feel of it. The horses will have to learn that you're in charge."

Stefan swallowed and sighed. His hands, wet with sweat, were slippery on the reins. "Where do I go?"

"Gerhard told me that a man up the street sells farm implements. Let's see what he has. I'll give you directions as we go."

Stefan took a deep breath and spoke his first command loudly. "*Schritt!*"

The wagon began to move forward with a jolt. Stefan looked at his father and smiled with the pleasure of his success.

———•———

The sun was setting when Stefan and his father crossed the Someşul River headed back to Scheindorf, their wagon loaded with the United States International Harvest Self-binder. It would make harvest easier and efficient for their many plots of land. Stefan was thinking what a difference a day could make.

"Papa, it's late—I know a place where we can set up camp and spend the night," Stefan said.

The judge raised an eyebrow. "How do you know this place?"

Stefan smiled as he remembered the gypsy wagons. "It's a long story, but a good one."

He pulled up the team.

"Why don't I tell it to you after we set up camp?"

CHAPTER SEVEN

"But to see her was to love her,
love but her,
and love her forever."
Robert Burns

Scheindorf
1932–1935

BURLY JOHAN HOEPFNER, his salt-and-pepper hair
dusted with ash, worked at the blazing forge. His massive
hands, the size of small hams, pumped the huge bellows,
fueling the fire with gulps of air. The forge burned at
760 degree Celsius. It was hot enough to melt iron, and
the temperature in the shop was unbearable.

Seventeen-year-old Stefan Revak watched the blacksmith work. He was drenched with sweat from the swel-
tering heat.

"Let's take a break," Johan announced. "The piece
needs to harden; then I'll work on it some more. I'll
have your latch repaired in no time."

The two men walked out the large, open double
doors of the shop to catch the morning breezes. Johan
towered over Stefan. Stefan pulled out a kerchief and

mopped his face. Johan did the same.

Johan passed Stefan a flask of water. Stefan drank deeply. The cool water tasted sweet.

He passed the flask back.

"Got to clear my throat of the smoke and soot—this usually does the trick," said Johan. "But I swear, sometimes at night, when I eat, all I can taste is soot. Drives Magdalena crazy when I don't like her food." He paused for a moment. "Of course, it would help if she didn't burn it all the time!"

His generous belly shook with laughter at his own joke. Stefan smiled.

"Don't tell her that now!"

"I won't."

Stefan looked down the street at St. Anne's and saw what looked like a small group of people, some young, others stooped with age, leave the church and walk down the stone steps. They clustered at the foot of the stairs for a moment, talking. Then Father Ettinger walked out and put his arm around a woman dressed in black.

It wasn't Sunday, there were no weddings scheduled, and this seemed odd. Stefan could feel the somber aura of the gathering from a distance. A funeral?

"What's happening at the church?" Stefan asked, pointing in the direction of St. Anne's.

"Oh, very sad. That's the Ditzig family."

The group left the church and walked down the street in the direction of the blacksmith's shop. Father Ettinger stood in front of the church and watched them walk away. He made the sign of the cross and walked up the stairs back into the chapel.

"They must be leaving the funeral of Mathilda. Poor Josef, in America all those years, lost his money in the depression, returns home penniless, and his daughter comes down with the fever and dies."

"How old was she?"

"She was six, I think." Johan paused and then looked off in the distance. "Losing a child is the most devastating thing that can happen to a parent. Your children are not supposed to die before you. It is the greatest loss in life. You never recover."

The trace of a tear traveled down Johan's soot-covered face leaving a clean trail. Stefan wondered. He wanted to ask more, but he did not want to pry.

They stood in silence as the procession passed. Stefan watched the family and friends walk slowly past them, their heads down. His heart ached for them. What if his father had never returned from America? What greater loss might he have known then? Stefan's thoughts turned dark with the possibilities of what might have been.

Stefan said a quick prayer and made the sign of the cross. The last member of the procession was a young girl. He thought she might be twelve or so. She had a slim frame and thick, curly dark brown hair that cascaded to her shoulders. She stood tall, wearing a dark dress, carrying a Bible, and walking slowly. When she looked in Stefan's direction, he saw her high cheekbones and full pink lips. She looked right through him as if she did not see him, her hazel green eyes wet with tears, then she turned away hugging the Bible tight to her chest.

Stefan stared, following her with his eyes as she walked away. His heart began to beat rapidly. She was the most beautiful girl he had ever seen.

"Who is she?" Stefan asked.

"That's Herr Ditzig's daughter, Maria."

"That's Maria?" Stefan could hardly believe the cute

little girl he used to see had so quickly turned into a striking young woman. "Frau Leili, her grandmother, lives across the road from us. I used to see Maria go there when her mother worked in the fields." Stefan paused as his eyes stayed locked on her. "I can't believe it. She's almost grown up. She's very pretty."

"Yes, she is," Johan replied.

Stefan was quiet for a moment. Then he spoke what was in his heart.

"Someday, she will be my wife."

"Stefan, you're crazy! She's only eleven, I'm sure of it. You're—what—seventeen now?"

Stefan stood his ground, his eyes never leaving the young woman.

"I will wait," he said.

Twelve-year-old Maria Ditzig picked up her skirts and ran through the tall grass in the field one late warm Sunday afternoon. On a dare, she was following the older boys Franz Moore, Martin Schimpf, and Stefan Müntz with her cousins, Henrike and Rosalia Leili and Theda Tepfenhardt, to a barn on the Revak property. She laughed to herself, pleased to be in on the secret, whatever it might be, as she was the youngest of the group.

The bank of fluffy clouds on the horizon, rimmed with dark gray, was turning deep pink with the setting sun. When they approached the barn, Franz put a finger to his lips to signal quiet.

As they drew nearer, Maria heard music. Someone was singing and playing the accordion. She recognized the song immediately. Her mother used to sing them to sleep with it. *"Guten Abend, Gut Nacht,"* the Brahms lullaby, floated from the barn. It brought back memories of her sister, and for a moment, she fought back tears. She missed Mathilda terribly.

Maria brushed the tears away with the back of her hand—no need for them to call her a baby. She wanted to be grown up.

Franz quietly opened the barn door. The baritone voice drew her in. It was beautiful, strong. The lyrics were sung with a tenderness that profoundly touched her heart. She stood in the doorway and listened.

"Maria, come! Come!" Franz whispered, motioning to her.

She followed the crowd and got there just in time to see Franz surprise the mysterious singer. "Who are you singing to?" Franz shouted up to the young man seated on the wagon.

Startled, Stefan Revak, the judge's son, abruptly stopped playing. He smiled self-consciously down at the cluster of young people who stood looking up at him. "Franz, why did you do that?"

"We wanted to have a little fun. It started with sneaking up on you!"

"Well, it worked," Stefan said, clearly annoyed—but laughing a little too. "You had fun at my expense. Once again, Franz."

Maria listened to the banter between the two friends. Stefan had always been in her life, but she had never really noticed him until now. He had grown tall and handsome. She looked at him and smiled, hoping he would notice her.

"Come on, Revak, our parents are in the wine cellar.

Can we stop the lullabies and love songs," Franz put his hands over his heart and pretended to swoon, "and get to polkas and dancing? Come on!"

From his perch on the wagon seat, Stefan's eyes locked on Maria's. She felt suddenly shy—as if he were seeing right into her. Her heart fluttered with a feeling of lightness she had never had before. The emotion vibrated through her body, startling her. She looked down, breaking their connection. She was uncertain of what to do or say.

"Come on, Revak, play!"

Saved by the music!

Stefan stood up and began to play a lively German polka. His right hand raced across the keyboard, and with his left hand, he pumped air through the bellows and played the bass notes and chords. The joyful music filled the barn. Everyone started clapping in time to the music. The girls and boys paired up and danced.

Maria laughed and watched the scene. Since she did not have a partner, she clapped and danced around by herself. Smiling, she looked up at Stefan and found him looking at her again. He was watching her dance, and he smiled and winked. She felt warm all over.

Young Stefan Revak was obsessed, and he knew it. Thoughts of Maria constantly distracted him. He worked in the fields and thought about her. Every time he walked into the village, he hoped he would run into her. He went to Mass and searched for her. He felt as if she had cast a spell over him. Feelings he had never known had been unlocked in his heart, and he rocked with emotions he did not understand. He hardly knew her, and yet he had known her all of his life. How could that be?

Sometimes he would wake up very early and think of her. He wanted to give her so much. He wanted to share his dreams with her—to make them happen together. He had so much to tell her. Yet he was torn about what to tell her. He wanted to open his heart, to share his past with her. Yet how could he talk about his mother's drinking? It was better now, but her drinking had scarred him as a child. Children should not have to live in fear of their parents—never knowing what might upset them. Drinking made his mother unpredictable and mean. How could he tell Maria these shameful things?

Other days he would wake up dreading the monotony of work on the farm. The cycle of work never changed. He wanted more for his own family. He wanted to manage the farm and properties as a business, not just as a man who labored in the field, never getting anywhere. How would he get there when he was trapped working for his father, who paid him nothing and gave him no land?

He felt guilty at the thought. Though his life was not what he wanted, it was better with his father home. So much better. How could he complain?

More and more, he realized that nothing was ever simple. Life was not black or white. Work was demanding, but having his father to help and give advice, and his mother happy again and not drinking, he had fallen into the rhythm of the seasons and their cycles and demands. Gone was the embarrassment that had dogged him in the days when his mother was the topic of village gossip, cast as a drunk and a sluggard. His family held a prominent role in the community. They were successful land and business owners. The wagoner and the blacksmith had made another large wagon and then a sleigh for the family. The sleigh held two people in the front and two in back. No one in the surrounding towns had anything like it.

Yet Stefan's journey to his dreams seemed to be taking forever. He had to have Maria, he decided. Maria was the key.

———•———

When he was not working the property, Stefan was in constant demand to sing and play the accordion for festivals and dancing. He loved singing and playing music. Not only did he enjoy watching people smile and laugh, but he could lose himself in the music. He could forget his worries. Music lifted his spirit and freed him from the chores of daily life.

Though he knew he was well liked by the girls of the village and admired by many of their fathers, he was not interested in any of them. He knew who he wanted to marry. Maria and her parents often came to the village dances. Since he was always playing, he could never dance with Maria, but he found time to talk with her when he took a break from the music. Her parents would watch from across the room.

One evening, Franz Moore, Martin Schimpf, and Stefan were invited to the home of the Tepfenhardt twins, Theda and Tilda, for a "spinning." The girls would be spinning flax fibers into thread. The blue-flowered flax plant, used for centuries for both its fiber and oil, was common in the area. The strong, fine threads were woven into linen fabrics.

They talked as they walked to the girls' home.

"So why are we going to this?" Stefan asked. Time was his most precious resource and he had little to spare, but his friends had urged him to go. He could not imagine why he would want to waste an evening watching girls spin flax fibers into thread. He could think of ten other things that were more important.

"You don't know?" Franz laughed. He leaned over to Stefan. "When a girl drops a spindle, which they do once in a while, one of us," he pointed to his chest, "is expected to pick it up."

"Sooooo?" Stefan asked.

"When you pick up a spindle and return it to the girl, your reward is a kiss."

"Oh, I get it now," Stefan said. "I really don't want to go. I've got a lot to do tomorrow." The barn and fences needed repair. He had errands to run for his father. This sounded childish. Besides, he was not interested in other girls. The farm and properties were his responsibility.

Stefan stopped in the street.

"Franz, I really don't want to go. I'm sorry. You two go and have fun. Tell me about it later. I've got to go."

"Stefan, wait," Franz said.

Stefan stopped and turned around.

"There's something we didn't tell you," Franz said.

Stefan was annoyed. Enough of this. He had an early start tomorrow.

Franz cocked his head to the side and smiled. "Maria Ditzig will be there." Franz paused. "But if you're too busy to go, I'm sure one of us would be happy to accept her kisses." Franz looked over at Martin, and they both nodded and laughed.

Uncontrollable jealousy roared through Stefan like a raging fire. The intensity of his response startled him. It took everything in his power not to show his feelings. He wanted to punch both of them. He took a deep breath and glared at Franz.

"Guess you're coming?" Franz said as if he could read his thoughts.

"You got me," Stefan shook his head. Then he laughed. "Yes, I'm coming."

Franz patted Stefan on the back. "I guessed as much."

The three young men walked to the house. Frau Tepfenhardt greeted them at the door.

"Welcome, boys. Come in." She led them to the candlelit room where the girls were already working on the flax fibers. The house smelled of beeswax, soap from freshly scrubbed floors, and apple pie. "Papa and I will be in the kitchen." She shook a warning finger at them. "Behave yourselves."

The boys settled on the wood floor and started to watch the process. Stefan sat cross-legged at Maria's feet. She looked down at him and smiled. Her hair, plaited into two long braids, hung down her back. She wore a white embroidered blouse with a pale blue smock.

While the other boys hovered around the twins, Stefan's eyes were for Maria alone. He watched entranced as her finely boned hands wound the flax fibers on the distaff's paddle. Then she took the distaff's long shaft and placed it in the crook of her left arm, balancing the paddle above her elbow. She gracefully drew the flax fibers from the paddle a few at a time and spun the thread by turning the spindle with her right hand. It was amazing to watch.

Theda interrupted Stefan's focus with a question.

"Stefan, you are near mandatory induction? Yes?"

It was a topic often in his thoughts these days—a change that was coming whether he liked it or not. "Yes, there should be about ten of us next year."

He looked up at Maria. She had stopped smiling.

"When I get the letter from the government, I will report like everyone else. It's my duty to serve in the Romanian army." He paused to gather his thoughts and perhaps make Maria smile again. "It shouldn't be too bad—might even be fun. An adventure with ten of us."

"I think it would be scary being so far from home," Theda said. She put down the distaff, and the spindle dropped to the floor. Franz quickly snatched it up and placed it in her right hand.

"*Danke*, Franz." She leaned over and gave him a kiss on the cheek.

Franz turned back to the rest of the young men with a gleam in his eye.

"Stefan, I'm sure your parents will worry about you," Maria said. "You're their only son."

Stefan started to respond, but Maria's spindle fell to the floor, rolling past him. He quickly crawled to it, scooped it up, and put it in her lap. On his knees, he leaned in close to her and whispered, "Will *you* miss me?"

She put both of her hands around his face and gave him a gentle kiss on the cheek. It was pure ecstasy.

She leaned back in her chair. He put his hand on his cheek where she kissed him. He saw her sadness as she looked into his eyes.

"Yes, I will miss you," she told him. "Very much."

Some weeks later, Stefan rode his bicycle to Maria's home and parked it near the white fence that bordered their yard. Today, the palms of his hands were damp with apprehension. What would he say to her parents? What would they talk about on this first official courting call?

As he walked to the porch, he noticed the colorful flowers that spilled out of the window boxes on either side of the front door. Should he have brought flowers? It was too late now.

Stefan had seen Maria at every village event, after Mass and at church events. They were rarely able to find time alone, but they did talk whenever they saw one another, and he could feel her attraction for him.

He knocked on the door, and then rubbed his sweaty palms on his pants.

Frau Ditzig answered his knock. Her round face, flushed from the heat of the day, broke into a smile when she saw him. "Come in, Stefan."

Frau Ditzig led him to a long narrow room simply furnished with a wooden table, rockers, and benches. The pine floor, covered with colorful braided rag rugs, creaked as they walked in.

Maria stood waiting. Time stopped at the sight of her. He smelled roses. Sun streamed through the filmy lace curtains on the windows, and she was illuminated by rays of light. She was smiling. He thought his heart would stop.

She had dressed up for him, and his mouth went dry as he took in the sight. She was wearing a long cream dress, the bodice embroidered with pink thread. Her dark hair, plaited and adorned with rose-colored ribbons, was wrapped around her head, framing her heart-shaped face. Her hazel eyes sparkled with laughter and happiness.

"You look beautiful," he said.

She smiled shyly and gave him a little curtsy, bowing her head. "Thank you, Stefan."

Maria gestured to a small, wooden bench at one end of the room. It was highly carved and brightly painted with flowers. She sat down, and Stefan joined her. Her mother sat in a rocker at the other end of the room and picked up her mending.

Uncomfortable, he rubbed his sweaty palms on his pants and glanced across the room to where Frau Ditzig sat. She looked up and smiled, then went back to her work.

Maria broke the awkward silence.

"Stefan, I've always wondered about America and your parents." She paused and looked down. "I hope I'm not being too direct, but didn't your mother live there for a while, then your father? Do you think that they will ever go back?"

Relieved that she had taken the lead, Stefan answered, "It's a long story, but I'll give you the short version." He smiled at her. "I can answer any questions you want, though."

Maria nodded, encouraging him to go on.

"Mama went to America first to work as a governess. She was there for three years. She has always wanted to live in America. She came back to marry Pop, and they planned to go back together. They married and got pregnant with me. They tried to go back, but because of immigration rules, they couldn't, because Mama was pregnant with me."

Maria's brow furrowed. "Why did they want to go to America? Leave their family. It is so beautiful here."

"Good question," Stefan said. At times, he had asked much the same question, but as he grew older, he understood better. "They have family here, their parents, but they have brothers and sisters in America. The family in America has done well. Both Mama and Pop feel that they can make a better life there. Pop likes business and politics more than farming. He thinks he can make more money and have a more fulfilling life in America. There is so much to do there."

"Like what?"

Stefan thought about his parents' many stories. "There are many businesses in the big cities. There is work to be found. Mama has talked about the theater, the shops, and the gardens. She loved the fine clothes—and being a farmer's wife is not what she dreamed of. She got a taste of America and has never stopped wanting to go back."

"So what do you think about this dream of theirs? Do you want to go to America?"

"We were supposed to leave, Mama and me, some years ago. Pop was working in America. We were here. Mama was in a very bad place."

Stefan stopped and hung his head. Frau Ditzig got up and left the room. Stefan followed her with his eyes. He sensed that she had heard the gossip about his mother, and he felt a rush of relief and a wave of gratitude when she left them alone.

"What do you mean?" Maria said gently.

Stefan lowered his voice. "Mama was drinking—a lot. Uncle Anton said that she drowned her sorrows in drink. She was very unhappy. She would drink instead of cook or clean. She slept during the day."

"And you were alone with her—you were very

young?"

"Yes, Pop left when I was five. He was gone for four years." Stefan stopped.

Maria sighed. "That's a long time to be without a father—or a husband."

"Papa's absence did not bring out the best in Mama."

They were both quiet. Stefan searched for the right words.

"When Mama drank, she didn't know how to stop. She would get angry. I think she was always angry that Pop was not there. That he was in America and she had to run the property and raise me all by herself. Sometimes she would take it out on me—even Uncle Anton."

"What do you mean?" Maria asked again, still gentle.

Stefan looked down. He was not ready to talk about this. "When she drank, she was a different person."

"So what happened? Why didn't you go to America to be with your father?"

"Papa sent us the money. Mama was so excited. I wondered what it would be like to leave everyone I knew—our home, my friends, our village. I wasn't sure I wanted to leave everything. But I was really young. What did I know? I would stay with my parents—whatever they decided."

"Why didn't you go?"

"Immigration law changed. A quota system allowed only so many people to go to America. We couldn't."

"So you do want to go to America?"

Stefan sighed. How could he put into words his thoughts and emotions?

"Farming is hard. I can tell you that. The work never ends, and if you aren't there to do it, it doesn't get done.

I had hoped to go on for more school when Pop came back, but he needs me to manage the land and livestock. Pop is busy as mayor and with the mill and his other business ventures. He can't do what he wants to do unless I work the land."

Stefan swallowed hard. He had to speak of the feelings that had been building since his father returned.

"Sometimes I feel stuck, trapped. My father follows his ambition, and as long as I work for him, he can do that. He has what he wants. But do I? Will I if I stay here? I want more for my family." Stefan stopped and looked in Maria's eyes. She looked back into his, and he saw understanding there. His heart lifted.

"I want to be a businessman. I know how to farm. I've done it all my life. But at this point, I have no land, no money to my name. I have to find another way to become independent. America may be that way."

As the last words escaped, Stefan felt as if a weight was lifted from his heart. He had finally let the dam of feelings spill free. He could not believe he had shared so much. And Maria . . . she had just listened. She did not judge. She was not the child he had expected, but a young woman. He felt as if he was catching up with someone he had always seen but did not really know.

"Let's go outside for a while. It's cooler out there," Maria said. She smiled, took his hand, and led him to the porch swing. They rocked back and forth in the swing, listening to the birds. Stefan could not believe he had told her so much so quickly. She was a wonderful listener.

He turned to her, and she looked at him and smiled.

"I like you," spilled from Stefan's lips. He could not help himself. He looked into her sparkling green eyes and wanted to fall into their depths forever. Did she feel the same?

She looked down and took his hand in hers.

"I like you too," she said and squeezed his hand. He looked at her small hand cradled in his larger one. Her hand felt soft and warm. He hoped she did not feel the rough calluses on his hands.

They were quiet for a moment.

"Stefan, I will see you—if you promise not to have any other girl but me."

He was surprised. He had underestimated this young woman. She was direct, and she knew what she wanted.

Maria continued, "If you can't promise me, then we should not see each other like this." She looked right at him. She was serious.

He was stunned. He had to promise or he would lose her.

He knew in his heart what to say. She was the only one for him.

"Maria, you'll be mine and I'll be yours—forever."

————— ◦ ◦ —————

Over the months that followed, Stefan and Maria were together at all of the village gatherings, church events, and dances. He knew that she was the perfect choice for him. She had a wonderful spirit. She was serious but lighthearted. She had an inner strength that he admired. She was the kind of woman who would be by his side, no matter what.

They were sitting on her front porch swing talking one day, alone. Frau Ditzig was in the kitchen. Stefan was not sure how to bring up the topic he feared most, but it was gnawing at him—growing into something between them that he couldn't let stay there. He remembered the relief he'd felt when he told her about his frustrations on the farm. How a weight had lifted. He needed that feeling again. He had to tell her.

He swallowed hard.

"I need to talk to you about something," Stefan said. "It's not easy for me to talk about it."

"Anything," Maria said. She smiled.

He shifted uncomfortably in his seat. "Remember when I first talked with you about my mother's drinking?"

She nodded and reached for his hand.

"This is hard for me," he said.

"It will be all right, Stefan," she said. "You can talk to me."

He swallowed again and looked at their hands locked together.

"It was hard for me—as a child. I never knew what to expect from my mother. I never knew if I would come home and find food for dinner or find her passed out in her bed."

Maria said nothing. She nodded.

"I lived in fear of her rage—that she would hit me— for the smallest thing. I could do nothing right. She thought I lied, stole from her. These were things I did not do, but the drink made her crazy."

He stopped for a moment.

"You have to understand that when Mama drank, I did not have a mother. I was lonely. I had no one to protect me except Uncle Anton. He couldn't be there all the time. He had his family and property to manage.

She drove him away, and he kept coming back. He's the one who finally wrote my father telling him to come home."

"I didn't know that," she said slowly.

"I don't know what we would have done without Uncle Anton."

Maria nodded.

"You have to understand that I lived in fear. I never want my children to ever have to live like I lived— ever!" Anger at his mother and the childhood he never had burned inside him.

He had never thought he would ever share this, but he had to—not only to relieve his burden, but for the sake of the future. He had thought long and hard, and he knew one thing: his children must never go through what he had gone through.

He swallowed hard, torn between embarrassment and his need to share the strength of his resolve. He had to tell her what he would never tolerate. She had to understand.

"I need to talk to you about drinking." He looked directly into her eyes and spoke, "I don't care if you drink wine—or even whiskey. If you get drunk once, okay, but if you get drunk the second time, that's it. Even if I love you, that's it."

Stefan watched Maria lean away from him. Her hand slipped out of his. Was this too much to ask? Would she understand?

Maria nodded. She turned back to look at him. There were tears in her eyes.

Stefan said more gently, "I promised myself I would never have a child go through what I went through."

For a moment, neither of them spoke. Stefan looked

away. "It's better now—now that Pop has been home. She's happier."

"But my life was miserable when he was away. When we were alone."

"I understand," Maria said. She took his hand. He turned to face her and saw compassion in her eyes. Then she spoke. "You won't have to worry about that with me."

She smiled at him. Comfort and peace filled his soul.

"We will work everything out, Stefan—every trouble, every dream. We will do it together. I promise."

His heart filled with love.

"You are my *Schatzie*," he said. Her eyes were radiant. He leaned over and tenderly kissed her. Her soft lips were warm and waiting.

CHAPTER EIGHT

"Your children are not your children.
They are the sons and daughters of Life's longing for itself."
Kahlil Gibran

Scheindorf to Baia Mare, Romania
1936

STEFAN RODE HIS bicycle home, parked it in the usual place by the wagons, and walked toward the house. The warm spring day was perfect for courting. Blue and yellow wildflowers blossomed along the road, and the first red poppies waved their heads in the wind behind the house, their bright red a contrast with the tall green grass. Pink cherry blossoms perfumed the air. Thoughts of Maria consumed him to distraction.

As he approached the porch, he saw his father and Uncle Anton talking. His father stood when he saw him. His look was stern, and Uncle Anton's customary smile was absent. Stefan slowed his steps. What was wrong?

His father held out an envelope.

"It's your letter from the army—I knew it would come soon. It is your year to be called to duty. Open it.

Let's see how soon you have to leave."

Stefan took the envelope, opened it, and read aloud, "I'm to report to the Baia Mare railway station no later than 5 p.m. on Monday, May 18. From there, we'll go to the city military grounds."

"Not much notice," Uncle Anton said. "Just ten days."

"This will upset your mother." Stefan's father shook his head in dismay. "But at least you'll be close by—it's only twenty-eight kilometers. If that's where they end up assigning you." He put his hand on his son's shoulder.

Stefan stared at the letter, and the words started to sink in. He had known it was coming, and he did feel a strong sense of duty to the Romanian army. Yet, this would separate him from Maria. The thought was devastating. Stefan did not know what to say.

"It's only sixteen months," Uncle Anton said. "Try to think of it as an adventure. You'll meet new people, learn new things—besides, Maria will wait for you. I've seen how she looks at you."

"Stop it, Uncle Anton," Stefan said. He felt a little embarrassed. "We're just friends."

"Ah-ha," his uncle responded. "Love is a wonderful thing. Life sometimes gets in the way."

"Let's go tell your mother." Stefan's father squeezed his shoulder and muttered, "I'm dreading this."

The draft took eleven young men from Scheindorf. For Maria, the ten days passed in a blur of activity. In between her chores, church, and their times together,

Maria knitted dark blue wool blanket. Each tight stitch
was made with love, her every hope that it would keep
him warm.

The day of departure finally arrived.

Maria joined the crowd that surrounded the two
wagons that would carry the young men to an uncertain
future. She prayed fervently as Father Ettinger gave his
blessing and sprinkled holy water on the young men.
She watched for Stefan, craning her neck, catching a
glimpse of him here and there in the throng of people.
She listened halfheartedly to his father's final words to
the recruits.

"Travel safe, men of Scheindorf. You and your fathers
before you have honored our country by serving in our
army. Take your training seriously. Be respectful of your
officers and fellow soldiers. Remember you represent our
village. Help each other. Make new friends."

He paused for a moment.

"And don't forget to write your mothers!"

The young men laughed.

"May God be with you and protect you."

Maria stood by her mother, clutching the blanket to
her chest, waiting for the moment when she could say
her last good-bye. The crowd started to thin as people
went back to home and work. Soon just the immediate
families surrounded the wagons. It was time.

Maria walked in the direction where Stefan and his
Uncle Anton sat—in the wagon where she had first
heard him sing. She could see him looking for her, and
she quickened her steps. He finally saw her and smiled.

Out of breath, she reached the wagon and held out
the blanket.

"I made this for you. It will keep you warm—and

remind you of someone who waits for you. I will pray for you every day."

Stefan leaned down to take the blanket from her. His warm dark eyes looked into hers, and her heart seized with grief. What would happen to him? Would he be safe? Would he think of her?

Tears ran down Maria's face. Stefan reached down and wiped a tear away.

"I will write to you," Stefan said.

"I will write every day."

"Time to go," Uncle Anton said.

She stepped away from the wagon. Stefan Müntz started to sing a familiar march, and Martin Schimpf and Franz Moore joined in. One by one, the young men who were leaving home for the first time joined their voices in song.

The wagons started to pull away. Maria felt as if her heart was being torn from her chest.

Why is it the hardest on those left behind?

———•◦•———

Hours later, Stefan focused on guiding the big grays down the steep grade to the Some ul River, using the wagon brake to ease their descent. The large wagon was heavy, full of men and supplies, and he needed to hold it back from the horses.

"Look, Stefan." Franz Moore leaned over, tapped him on the shoulder, and pointed. "Roma!"

Stefan looked up at the familiar spot. Sure enough, there was a camp of five brightly painted miniature houses. Stefan brought the wagon to a stop at the ferry landing and stood up to survey the scene. Children played around the wagons, and dogs barked in warning. Horses grazed in the meadow. The smell of wood smoke from the cooking fires drifted their direction. He smelled roasted rabbit.

"We'll take the small wagon across first," Herr Moore called out.

"Understood," Stefan called out. Uncle Anton got out of the wagon to help Herr Moore.

Stefan passed the reins to Franz. He smiled with anticipation. Was Cappi here? Lash and Macalla? It seemed like a lifetime ago that he and his mother had met the gypsies and accepted a ride in their wagon.

"Watch the horses, will you, Franz? I have something I need to do."

Without waiting for an answer, Stefan jumped down from the wagon and walked in the direction of the camp. He could hear voices raised in song coming from the camp, children laughing, and the rush of water from the river.

"What are you doing?" Franz called after him. "You can't go over there! They're the untouchables!"

Stefan laughed to himself and approached the nearest wagon. Two men were sitting around a fire, smoking and watching the children play. They looked up suspiciously, as Stefan approached. One of the men put his hand in warning on his belted hunting knife but did not move.

Stefan asked in Romanian, "Do you know of a man named Cappi? We're about the same age. He's the son of Lash and Macalla."

"What do you want with this man Cappi—there are many Roma by that name."

"He's my friend. We met years ago, and I haven't

seen him since."

The man with the hunting knife stood up. He towered over Stefan. Bushy black eyebrows crowned his dark coal eyes, and his auburn hair and beard were long and curly. His eyes narrowed as he appraised Stefan

Stefan stepped back.

"Stay here." The man held out his hand to stop him. "Reva, keep an eye on this *gadža*," he said in a threatening sneer. "I don't trust him."

Stefan watched the tall man walk to a blue-painted wagon, the window's once-bright yellow trim now peeling and worn. He disappeared for a few minutes.

While he waited, Stefan wondered if he had asked for trouble by stopping.

In a few minutes, the man returned with a shorter gypsy. As they approached, Stefan recognized Cappi's raven hair, chiseled features, and crooked nose.

"Is that you, Stefan, after all these years?" Cappi spoke in Romanian. Smiling, he reached out his hand and latched on to Stefan's outstretched arm.

"Sounds like you've picked up Romanian," Stefan said.

Cappi nodded. "Some Romanian, some Hungarian— maybe even a little German." He gave Stefan a friendly punch in the arm. They both laughed.

"Who are you traveling with?" Cappi asked, looking past Stefan to the wagons full of curious young men.

"These are all friends from Scheindorf. We've been called up for our mandatory service in the Romanian army. We have six weeks of training to go to in Baia Mare."

Stefan did not say it was his first time away from home, but he thought it. It was going to be an adventure, but a lonely one.

"Going to be a soldier, huh?" Cappi said. "I've got a new job too, since we last met."

"What's that?" Stefan asked.

"Let me show you," Cappi said. Together, they walked toward the blue wagon. Cappi asked about Gertrude. They both laughed, remembering her obvious fear of riding with gypsies. Stefan explained that his father had returned from America. Cappi seemed to understand how much that meant to him.

When they reached the wagon, Cappi turned to Stefan and said, "My parents both died—during the winter last year. They both started to cough up blood. It didn't take long." He hung his head in sorrow.

Stefan was stunned by the news. Cappi was young. His parents were young. Though life with his parents was not perfect, he could not imagine life without them.

"I'm sorry, Cappi," Stefan said and looked into his friend's eyes. "I'm very sorry."

"At least they died together," Cappi said. "They were so close; they could never have lived without the other. It was true love. You know?"

Stefan nodded, sobered by the story.

There was so much of life ahead. Life without those you love would be empty.

"Let me show you what makes me happy these days." Cappi climbed inside of the wagon and motioned for Stefan to follow.

Inside, Stefan's eyes quickly adjusted to the gloom. He was taken aback at the sight of a lovely young woman, her long, dark hair held back in a red-and-yellow printed scarf, sitting on a bed of straw, holding a baby. She smiled at Stefan.

"Stefan, this is my wife, Florica. Florica—this is my friend, Stefan." Cappi reached down and gently took a sleeping baby from Florica's arms. "And Stefan, this is my son. This is Lasho."

Stefan looked at the newborn baby. All of the babies Stefan had seen were pink and chubby. This baby was pale and thin with bluish lips. He seemed to have trouble breathing. Wrapped in a tattered and soiled blanket, the baby looked sick. Stefan's heart fell in worry. How could this child survive the bitterly cold winter in a wagon?

"Stefan, we need to go!" He heard Franz call. "Stefan!"

"I have to go," he said. "But I have something for you."

Without another thought, Stefan ran back to the wagon and grabbed Maria's warm wool blanket. He ran back to Cappi and Florica's wagon and climbed back in. He held out the beautiful new blanket.

"Florica and Cappi, my gift to your son. May it keep him warm over many cold winters—and may you always remember our friendship."

Cappi translated to Florica as her eyes filled with grateful tears, and she smiled.

———•—•———

Later that afternoon, Stefan and Uncle Anton guided the loaded wagon to the Baia Mare Railway Station. The grimy station, stained by years of coal smoke, was jammed with trains, wagons, and hundreds of men awaiting the same fate. The young men from Scheindorf gathered their belongings and jumped from the wagons.

A sharp whistle of authority cut through the chaos.

Stefan looked around to find the source. A tall officer in full military dress stood on the second-story balcony of the building overlooking the square. The swarming chaos slowed for a moment as men jostled for position, trying to catch a glimpse of the man blowing the whistle. Then they quieted in anticipation of what might be next.

The officer shouted in Romanian, "Were all of you born in 1914?"

Confusion erupted, as some men did not hear the question while others did not understand Romanian.

"Fall in, five across, facing to my right, and wait for me," the officer shouted and left the balcony.

"I guess this is good-bye," Stefan said to Uncle Anton. "Please give my parents my love." They quickly hugged.

"Just keep your nose clean and follow orders," Anton said. "You'll do just fine. Hard work you're used to—and you're in good shape, unlike some of these city boys." Anton nodded his head in the direction of a few heavy conscripts. He smiled, and Stefan laughed.

The comment was appreciated but unnecessary. Stefan had already made up his mind to make the best of this time in the army. He would learn from it. It would expose him to life away from home, and as his father had said, it would make him stronger.

"Thanks for everything, Uncle Anton," Stefan said. He clapped his uncle on the shoulder and walked in the direction of the men who were lining up.

After minutes of confusion, disorderly columns of men followed an officer through the city, across the Săsar River Bridge to the walled army post. The Romanian flag of blue, yellow, and red flew atop the gate entrance. Five armed sentries stood at attention. A sign announced the First Infantry Division Headquarters, *Divizia 1 Infanterie Sediul Central.*

Suddenly it was real.

The officer in charge stopped the marching men with three quick blasts from his whistle. He waited until the group quieted, then spoke. "I will call names alphabetically. When I call your name, step forward and present the letter you received with your orders. When you enter the compound, you will be given the number of your company and platoon. Once inside, find your platoon sergeant major."

Stefan waited for his turn as one by one, young men entered the gate and disappeared into the compound.

"Revak, Stefan," the officer called. Stefan walked quickly in the direction of the officer. The sentry gave him a cursory look and told him he was in Company Eight, Third Platoon, and pointed in the direction of a knot of men clustered to the right.

Later that night, Stefan lay in his upper bunk listening to the snores of the man below him. He had folded his new khaki infantry tunic, shirts, socks, and breeches. Brown leather hiking boots and a canvas bag, a dark green enamel mess tin, a gas mask in its olive drab bag, a canteen, a helmet, and other gear were stowed away.

Stripped of his civilian clothes, he lay on a well-worn mattress covered by an army-issued wool blanket, wearing his new rough underwear. Tonight, for the first time in his life, he would be sleeping with strangers. He had entered the domain of the Romanian army.

———•••———

Basic training lasted six weeks without leave. Though Stefan and Maria wrote to each other, the mail was slow, and days would pass without any word.

Stefan's military training consisted of learning how to march in formation, taking language classes, and weapons training. Since he had grown up in a German home, was already fluent in Romanian, and lived in a village that was often located in Hungary as the borders shifted, he was fluent in languages the other recruits were not. He ended up serving as a language tutor. Marching and weapons came naturally to him, and as Uncle Anton said, he knew how to work hard. The six weeks went by quickly.

He returned to Scheindorf for two weeks of leave. His parents were happy to see him. All his father could talk about was the German cultural center underway in the village. The cultural center was truly an international effort, with Scheindorf citizens and those who had immigrated to America donating money for the building. The young people of the community had contributed some one hundred beech logs for the building's walls. If all went well, the building would open in the fall.

Stefan was delighted to be home for the annual Festival of St. Anne, traditionally held on her feast day, July 26. There was music and dancing, food and wine. When Stefan wasn't playing the accordion, he and Maria danced. They spent every moment possible with each other, juggling their time between the families, but soon leave was over. It was another heartbreaking good-bye.

CHAPTER NINE

*"The only real mistake is the one from which
we learn nothing."*
Henry Ford

Baia Mare, Romania
1936

STEFAN RETURNED TO the Romanian army camp in Baia Mare to serve the remaining months of his service with his two most precious possessions—his bicycle and accordion. The bicycle would give him the freedom to travel home, some twenty-eight kilometers, when he could, and the accordion would help pass the time and perhaps help make some new friends. When he finished with his military obligation, he planned to talk with his father about setting up a business that he could manage, and he would ask Maria to marry him.

Upon his return to camp, he was assigned the job of *Frontasch*, taking care of the horses and stables. The job was familiar, he felt a kinship with horses, and he could do it well. The horses needed exercise, so he could ride as much as he wanted. He was in charge of grooming, feeding, and tending to their minor injuries. The stables needed regular cleaning, the manure shoveled, and the hay in the stalls replaced with fresh. While the troops were in the field, the trumpeter had a special signal to summon him, and he would race out on his best horse to help an injured soldier or horse or provide fresh mounts.

About seventy-five horses belonged to some forty soldiers. Stefan got to know many of the men. A number of them shared Stefan's special love of horses.

One day, while Stefan was in the stable cleaning the hooves of a chestnut mare, he heard a familiar voice.

"Stefan, where are you? I've come to check on Amadeus."

Stefan smiled at his friend's voice. He put down the mare's foot and stood up, slipped the hoof pick in his leather tool belt, then stroked her back and walked through the stall door, latching it behind him.

"Lieutenant Ștefănescu," he said, striding toward the voice. "I'm glad you're here."

The lieutenant reached out his hand to shake Stefan's. "How's he doing?"

"He's healing well," Stefan said. "Come on over and take a look." Stefan led the way down the hay-packed center of the whitewashed paddocks. As they passed, curious horses raised their heads, nodding and nickering at the men.

Amadeus heard them coming and snorted in greeting, tossing his long, curly black mane.

The lieutenant reached out to stroke the magnificent jet-black horse, whose forehead blazed with one white star. The horse nuzzled his head into his rider's chest.

"He's brilliant in the field," Ștefănescu said. "He's a genius. He needs no direction."

"Just like his namesake?" Stefan said. Stefan knew

that Ştefănescu was a great admirer of the composer Mozart and had named his horse after the prodigious and prolific musician.

"Just like his namesake," Ştefănescu said, smiling and continued to stroke his horse.

Stefan smiled. He enjoyed watching the deeply familiar and touching ancient bond between man and horse. It was the best part of being a soldier.

Some evenings when the men settled into their barracks, Stefan would play the accordion. The men would sing, and some would dance. One night, while he played and his fellow soldiers sang, the door of their barracks flew open. Stefan realized how late it was and quickly hid the accordion under his bunk.

"Who was playing? I heard music coming from here," the corporal said. "Who was it?"

No one said a word.

Stefan stood up. "It was me, sir. I was playing the accordion."

"Identify yourself, soldier."

"Frontasch Revak, sir." Stefan kept calm, but he was worried. Was music an infraction somehow? Or was he simply causing a disturbance too late at night?

"Corporal Schwartz," the soldier returned the introduction.

To his surprise, Corporal Schwartz pulled up a chair and sat down.

"Play it for me. Can you play 'Die Lorelei'?"

"Yes sir," Stefan said. He started to breathe again,

and his heart stopped hammering. He pulled his accordion out from its hiding place.

"Play, play!" the corporal said and waved his hand.

Stefan looked around the room at his bunkmates, who were as confused as he was. He shrugged his shoulders and played the tune. The corporal tapped his foot in time to the music.

When the song was over, Schwartz stood up, gave a short curt bow, and said, "Thank you for the concert. Now, don't play too loud or too late!"

With that, he turned around and left.

The next night, after dinner, a soldier came to the barracks and asked for Revak.

Stefan stood up. "Revak, Stefan, sir."

"Sergeant Major Grün wants to see you in his quarters at 1900 hours."

Stefan nodded, trying not to show concern. His sergeant wanted to see him. Why?

When seven o'clock arrived, he knocked on the door of the officer's quarters.

Sergeant Major Grün opened the door. "Where is the accordion?" he asked bluntly.

"I didn't know I was supposed to bring it." Stefan was confused.

"Go, get it. Bring it here."

Stefan was nervous now. *What will I tell Pop if they confiscate my accordion?*

He went back to the barracks, picked up the accordion, and reluctantly returned to the officer's quarters, expecting to lose his most prized possession. Corporal Schwartz opened the door.

"Come in, Frontasch Revak," he said grinning. "Glad you could make it."

Stefan was confused.

Grün held out three passes. "Come on, let's go," he said. "We're going to go and have some fun. We're going into town—get some good drink, food, maybe meet some girls?" He smiled at Stefan.

Stefan could not have been more surprised.

When the three soldiers walked into town, the lights, laughter, and music drew them to a busy tavern. The smoke-filled, dark-paneled room with red-checkered curtains smelled like beer, bratwurst, and sauerkraut. The room was packed with soldiers drinking, laughing, and flirting with pretty girls in colorful dresses.

One of the soldiers recognized Stefan. He got up and grabbed him by the arm, drawing him into the crowded room.

"Clear a space!" he shouted over the din. "Our entertainment has arrived!"

Stefan looked at his sergeant for approval. The sergeant nodded and smiled.

"Barkeep," the soldier called over the noise. "Beers for these three men!"

Stefan played the accordion and sang, and many of the boisterous crowd danced to the polkas he played. The patrons bought him drinks, toasted him, and applauded his music, frequently requesting their favorite songs and singing along.

Liquor flowed freely. The evening passed in a blur, and it was late when the three men said their goodnights and started to head back to camp. While walking down the main street, Sergeant Grün saw the lights still on in a nearby tavern, and he motioned toward it.

"One more drink, eh?" he said.

Stefan had been drinking more than usual and his head was starting to spin, but what could he say to his sergeant?

The tavern was empty except for two civilians sitting in the back. The soldiers sat at a table near the bar and ordered beers from the barkeep. Stefan played his accordion, playing lullabies and love songs, and Corporal Schwartz sang.

One of the civilians came up to their table and said, "Hey, Frontasch, come to my table and play for me."

Stefan laughed and said, "I can't. I'm under orders from my superior officer—ask him if he'll let me go. I'll play for anyone!"

The civilian walked over to Grün, roughly pulled him up by the collar, and began to punch him in the face. Grün's head rocked from side to side with the force of the blows. Shocked by the sudden assault, Stefan put down the accordion, grabbed the civilian, and dragged him out of the bar into the street.

Grün and Schwartz followed Stefan out of the tavern. The civilian was sitting in the street where Stefan had left him. Sergeant Grün made a lunge for the man, but Schwartz grabbed him and held him back.

"You've had enough to drink," Schwartz said to Grün. "Time to go." He grabbed his fellow officer by the arm and began dragging him away.

Grün shot a venomous look back at the man in the street. "We'll see about that," Grün said. He used his handkerchief to wipe blood from his mouth. A cut on his eyebrow bled profusely.

They headed back to the barracks down empty, dark streets, lit only by an occasional streetlight. His head still spinning, Stefan felt shaken by the sudden violence.

"I'll get that bastard," Grün muttered as they walked to the camp.

At the gate, Grün said, "Wait here." He walked into camp, unsteady on his feet, weaving back and forth, losing his balance, and stumbling now and then.

"What is he up to?" Stefan said to Schwartz.

"He's drunk."

Grün returned with two soldiers and two armed guards. He waved for Stefan and Schwartz to accompany them. Uneasily, they did.

Now seven men walked down dark, empty streets back to the tavern. When Stefan and Grün entered, the civilian spotted them immediately. In a drunken rage, he rushed over, grabbed Grün by the collar, and started punching his face again. Stefan pulled the civilian off Grün and dragged him back out of the tavern to the street.

"Will you stop?" Stefan urged the man, roughly pushing him to the ground. "You're going to get hurt!"

Stefan could hardly see straight. It was late, he was exhausted, and the liquor was catching up with him.

Behind him, the sergeant appeared in the tavern doorway. Wiping blood from his mouth, Grün ordered Stefan, "Hit him until I tell you to stop!"

Stefan hesitated. He looked at the sergeant, questioning him without words. This was insane. But the man was his superior officer. He had no choice.

"Do it! I'm giving you a direct order. Do it!"

Grün walked over and started viciously kicking the man.

"Hit him until I tell you to stop!" Grün screamed. "Hit him!"

Reluctantly, Stefan obeyed. The civilian curled up, his hands over his head, trying to protect himself. Schwartz joined them, and the three drunken soldiers attacked together, kicking, and punching.

Stefan stopped. This was wrong.

The man stopped groaning in pain. He was still.

"Enough, stop—let's go," Grün said. "I'm tired."

Stefan looked around at the empty street. The other soldiers and guards were gone. The civilian still did not move.

It was about five in the morning when they got to their respective quarters. Stefan's hands were bloody and bruised; his head throbbed. He quickly washed up, splashing water on his face, scrubbing his hands clean of the blood. His heart was pounding. One thought haunted him: what had they done?

———◆———

The newspaper article reported the death of a local civilian, describing the assailants as a soldier with an accordion and two others. Stefan dropped the paper. *My God, we killed him!*

The implications of it flooded through him. His life was over. What would Maria think? His parents? How could he ever look at himself in the mirror again? And what would happen to him? Surely, he would be arrested and charged, and he would face life in prison as a murderer.

Stefan continued his duties with the horses the next day, all the while wondering when he would be caught. Concentration was hard to come by, but maneuvers would soon begin, and there was work to do.

Focused on cleaning the stables, Stefan did not see the man enter.

"Frontasch Revak, the platoon leader wants to see you. Clean up and show up in his office within the hour."

"Yes, sir," Stefan replied, his stomach tied in knots. He quickly finished the necessary work, cleaned up, and went to see the platoon leader.

He knocked at the door.

"Enter!"

Stefan walked in. His platoon leader, Major Schneider, and a platoon leader from another company, a man by the name Filip Dobrona, whom Stefan knew from a village near Scheindorf, sat waiting for him. Major Schneider glared at Stefan through his monocle, and a sneer of disgust curled his lips. He said nothing.

Dobrona stood up. He was holding the newspaper. His serious blue eyes bored into Stefan's. The silence was sobering.

Dobrona read the newspaper article aloud. When he was finished, he dropped the paper and looked directly at Stefan. Stefan hung his head, his heart pounding. He wished the night was only a nightmare. But it was real. There was no going back now.

"Stefan, no one here has an accordion but you." Dobrona walked away from Stefan and sat, leaning on the desk. "I tell you this; I will help you as much as I can, if you tell the truth. If you lie, I cannot help you. Tell the truth, you'll come out of this all right, and you won't have to worry about it."

Stefan looked up, faint hope pricking at his heart. Was it true—could Dobrona help him? His voice choking with emotion, Stefan told them the story.

"Sir, I was acting under orders from a superior officer—what was I to do?"

The officers looked at one another. Major Schneider cleared his throat. "Go back to the stables," he said. "Get ready for maneuvers.

Stefan left, his heart filled with dread. What would happen now he had no way to know.

———•—————

The next morning, Stefan left on maneuvers. The troops walked two days to the wooded location where they would practice their war games. He had plenty of time to think about what might happen. The ten days of maneuvers were physically and mentally daunting— hauling their equipment, food, and water; setting up a field camp; cooking over an open fire; managing the horses; and artillery training and exercises.

During the two-day walk back to base, Stefan was exhausted from lack of sleep, his body ached, and he feared the consequences of his actions. A man was dead, and even if he had only been following orders, he was still responsible. He could be facing life in prison. He would lose Maria.

He prayed for forgiveness, and he prayed for help.

He was twenty-one.

———◆◆———

All the next week, consumed by worry, Stefan went through the motions of his work with the horses, finding little comfort in their presence. None of the usual officers came to visit. He wondered if everyone knew what had happened. Left alone and in silence with his shame, his mind worked overtime.

Finally, he was ordered to report to the platoon leader.

When he walked into the room, there were four officers seated behind a long table with an empty seat in the center. Sergeant Major Grün and Corporal Schwartz stood before them, waiting. Stefan walked over and stood next to Grün. He glanced at Grün. Grün stared back. His cuts had healed, but his black eye was still purple. His nose was crooked from being broken. Grün's eyes mirrored Stefan's fear.

The door opened, and Major Schneider entered the room in his field uniform, wearing kidskin gloves and spit-shined black boots, and carrying his riding crop. The three men stood at attention to face their judges.

Major Schneider sat down at the center of the table and slapped his crop down in front of him. Stefan's heart was racing. The hard faces of the officers before them were stern and angry. Stefan knew the platoon leader Dobrona and Lieutenant Ştefănescu. However, the other two officers he did not recognize. Ştefănescu would not look at him.

"This hearing will now begin," Major Schneider said.

Major Schneider picked up his pen. Then he slammed it down on the table. His face was red, his jaw tight with rage. He got up from the table and circled around the three men, pointing his finger in their faces, yelling and screaming, "What were you thinking? You are soldiers in the Romanian army—not hoodlums!" Major Schneider raised his hand as if to hit Schwartz but stopped. Stefan was shaking. The words blurred in his head. He dreaded what was going to happen. They must have decided to turn them over to the police. They were going to prison for the rest of their lives. They were an embarrassment to their company.

Major Schneider stood nose to nose with Grün.

"You idiot!" he screamed, spitting into his face. "You are a disgrace to this company!" He walked, circling around him. "Your lack of discipline and drunken temper make you unfit to serve." He turned his back to Grün for a moment and then rushed in close, face-to-face. "What were you thinking? Beating a civilian? Public drunkenness? You are an officer! We are not thugs. You disgust me!"

"Sir, I was—" Grün started to say when the major slapped him hard across the face. His head whipped back with the force of the blow. His nose started to bleed.

Stefan's heart throbbed in his throat.

"Sir, I was only trying to explain," Grün said.

The major lashed out with his black leather-gloved fist, punching Grün in the nose and knocking him to the ground. Blood spurted from his nose and mouth. The major looked down at the man, and his lips twisted in scorn. Then he kicked him in the chest.

The major left Grün writhing in pain on the floor. He walked back to his chair and sat down at the long table. He took off his bloodstained gloves and laid them carefully on the table. He leaned back in his chair, and his eyes glared at the two standing men.

Stefan was next.

Ştefănescu slowly got up from the table and pushed in his chair. He walked around the other officers, stood in front of Stefan, and leaned back on the table. His serious eyes met Stefan's.

Stefan, consumed by guilt and embarrassment in front of this lieutenant who had become a friend, dropped his head.

Sergeant Grün got up off the floor and stood next to Stefan. He mopped the blood from his face with a handkerchief.

When Ştefănescu spoke, his voice was firm and even.

"Stefan, look at me."

Stefan looked up and met his eyes.

"Tell us what happened."

Stefan explained what happened, the same as he had told Major Schneider and platoon leader Dobrona weeks earlier.

"Sir, I only did what I was commanded—nothing else."

Ştefănescu turned to the sergeant.

"Is this the truth?"

"Yes, sir," Grün said. "It was my doing. Revak only did what I ordered him to do. So did Corporal Schwartz. They were obeying my orders."

Major Schneider got up from his chair, picked up his riding crop, and slowly walked around the table to face the three men. It took everything in Stefan's power to stand tall, and he took a deep breath to steady himself.

Schneider's blue eyes were cold and hard as flint. He

made eye contact with each man, one by one.

"You men are imbeciles."

He paused and walked behind them.

"But you are lucky. The man you butchered did not die."

He paused again to let his words sink in. Stefan was confused, his mind numbed by worry. He did not understand the words at first. The man was not dead? They were not murderers? Hope began to trickle into his heart.

"The so-called 'civilian' you beat was not a civilian but an officer, a lieutenant from another company." Schneider circled them, a vulture closing in on its carrion. "You will pay him a visit. You will apologize for your actions." He slapped his riding crop across his hand in warning. "But that is not the end of your punishment— it is just the beginning."

The major sentenced Stefan and Corporal Schwartz to one week in the army brig, while Sergeant Grün received thirty days. When the injured lieutenant left the hospital, he served sixty days for being out of uniform and starting the fight.

Stefan accepted his punishment with relief. His monastic cell, furnished with a wood bench and a bucket, was cold. His uniform jacket became his pillow and his coat a blanket. He saw no one except the soldier who delivered his rations and periodically emptied his waste bucket.

In the long, dark nights, his sleep was plagued by nightmares of what might have happened: life in prison, his agony if Maria married another man, his father's disappointment and shame. Every waking moment was spent thinking about lessons learned and how this must never happen again. He thanked God for protecting him. He prayed for the man they had injured. His heart filled with gratitude. He had been given his life back.

One thing came as a surprise: his rations while in solitary confinement were officially ordered to be bread and water. Somehow, he received standard prison food. The week of punishment was a small price to pay. It went by quickly.

Once out of the brig, Stefan returned to his duties with the horses and the stables. Often he would take a team of horses with a wagon to buy hay, oats, wheat, and other supplies. Keeping the horses fed and healthy and the stables clean and in good repair was a busy job. Occasionally he was able to drive the wagon to Scheindorf, pick up supplies, and visit Maria and his parents.

His relationship with Ştefănescu remained solid. Though they never again talked about the incident in town, Stefan would never forget it.

For both men, Stefan's bicycle came in handy. Ştefănescu would ride the bicycle alongside the men while they were walking or marching in training. On weekends, when work was finished around 5 p.m. on Saturday, Stefan would ride his bicycle the twenty-eight kilometers home to see Maria. The last train to Scheindorf left the station at 2 p.m., giving him no other way to get there. When the weather was good, the trip was not bad. But the winter months were bitterly cold, and travel home became more and more difficult.

Since he had to be back to work by 5:00 a.m. on Monday, and he wanted to spend as much time as possible with Maria, he would leave after midnight. Riding at night on roads that were sometimes icy, with rocky and uneven terrain, was dangerous. But nothing—not even illness or injury—would keep him away from his beloved Maria.

CHAPTER TEN

*"Happy is the man who finds a true friend, and
far happier is he who finds that true friend in his wife."*
Franz Shubert

Scheindorf
Late Summer and Fall 1937

STEFAN RODE HIS bicycle home from Baia Mare for
the last time on a late summer day in August. The sun
warmed the air, the sky was bright blue, and the trees
were full of chirping birds. With the accordion strapped
to his handlebars, the soldier-minstrel sang joyfully as
he pedaled his way along the tree-lined road to Scheindorf. It was a beautiful day.

He was free. Discharged from the Romanian army
on August 27, he had completed his long-term obligation.
Two weeks a year, he would devote to the Romanian
army reserves.

Stefan felt lighthearted for the first time in his memory. His whole life lay before him.

His active mind once again considered his goals. He
wanted to be his own man with his own business, not
just a farmer. He desperately needed Maria to be his

147

wife. He knew he would have to balance his obligations to his parents and the farm with the responsibilities of his marriage and the new family that would be his. A world of possibilities stood before him, and he would tackle the obstacles one by one.

The trip home passed in a blur, his thoughts consumed by planning, and soon the white spire of St. Anne's appeared on the horizon. Stefan's heart beat faster. First things first: the visit to Herr Ditzig to secure his blessings.

Stefan wove his bike through the narrow streets, waving to friends as he passed. Soon he was at the Ditzig home. The brown, fluffy goslings that poked around the yard were getting big enough that their parents let them roam, no longer concerned about the hawks that could pounce and kill. The geese honked a warning when they saw him come near and scurried to herd their flock. The window boxes were full of the familiar red geraniums that Maria and her mother carefully tended.

He parked the bike at the foot of the steps and straightened his uniform jacket, composing his thoughts. How would he begin? What would Herr Ditzig say? His confidence fell for a moment as he considered the possibility of rejection, but his heart would never accept no for an answer.

He strode toward the front door and then abruptly changed direction. Likely Herr Ditzig would be at the weaving shop adjacent to the family home.

Stefan was right. Josef Ditzig was seated at the loom, his feet on the treadles, weaving lavender and white threads into cloth. The sunlit room, filled with swirling clouds of fabric dust, was quiet with the exception of the clicking and swishing of the loom. Herr Ditzig, a stout man with thick wavy brown hair, was focused on his work. He did not see Stefan immediately.

"Excuse me, Herr Ditzig, may I speak to you?"

Josef swung around on his seat, gave Stefan a broad smile, and stood up. "Stefan, are you home now?" They met halfway, and Herr Ditzig reached out his hand to shake Stefan's.

Stefan wanted to smile back, but to his surprise, all of a sudden, his confidence failed him as he was struck by the importance of this moment.

Nearly speechless, he managed to say, "Home for good, sir—what a relief. Time to get on with my life."

Herr Ditzig nodded in understanding.

Stefan's mouth went dry, and his palms were sweating. He swallowed hard and said tentatively, "May I have a word with you, sir?"

Herr Ditzig's eyes twinkled. "About Maria?"

"Yes, sir." Stefan paused to take a breath, and his heart spoke for him. "I love her more than anyone in the world. I think she feels the same about me." He paused to check Herr Ditzig's reaction—so far so good. "I would like to ask for her hand in marriage. With your blessings, of course." Stefan had run out of words.

Herr Ditzig nodded, and his gray eyes met Stefan's. "Marriage is a serious thing. You're in love now. But there will be hard times. You will need to work through those times."

"I will, sir. I will take care of her. She is the best thing that ever happened to me."

Herr Ditzig smiled again. "Maria's mother and I are fond of you, Stefan. You are a hard worker. You can take care of a family—we've seen that over the years. If Maria says yes, then you have our blessings." With an even bigger smile, Josef reached out his hand to shake Stefan's once again.

Stefan was dizzy with joy. He shook his future father-in-law's hand again quickly and had to hold himself back from racing from the room to find Maria.

"Where might I find her, sir? I would like to ask her now if I may."

Josef nodded. "Last time I saw her, she was in the sunflower fields."

"Thank you, Herr Ditzig!"

Stefan turned and walked quickly out the door, then broke into a run toward the fields.

"Maria, Maria!" he called as he raced up and down the rows of sunflowers that towered over his head. "Maria!" He could not see her anywhere.

"Over here!" her lovely, familiar voice called back. "Stefan, follow my voice."

Heart full to overflowing, he followed her voice and found her with a hoe in her hands, weeding. Her curly brown hair was captured in a green babushka, and her face was flushed from work and smudged with dirt. He thought he had never seen anyone so beautiful.

"Stefan, you're home!" She dropped the hoe and held out her arms.

He ran to her and held her close. Then he covered her face with kisses—her forehead, her cheeks, then her lips, tasting salty skin and her sweet softness. He would never have enough of her. She was living water for his thirst. His heart was pounding.

They broke away from the kiss. Her face was radiant, her hazel eyes shining as they looked into his. He slipped the babushka from her hair, and her long, dark hair fell to her shoulders.

"I have missed you so much." He stroked her hair, and then held her close again. "You will marry me, won't you? As soon as possible? I can't live another day without you."

———•———

The next few months flew by for Stefan and Maria. St. Anne's Catholic Church announced the marriage bans, and the date was set for November 15. Though no one in the town was surprised to see the couple wed, a few young girls and one father, in particular, were disappointed. Herr Weiss, the owner of one of the three village stores, was very fond of Stefan and had hoped he would marry his daughter and become his partner. Even so, he shook Stefan's hand and congratulated him good-naturedly enough.

Stefan worked wherever he was needed—planting the winter wheat with the hired hands, grooming the horses, running errands for his father. He renewed his friendship not only with merchants and tradespeople in town but with his young friends, including Cappi. When Stefan was not working, he was playing the accordion and singing at dances, family events, and festivals, sometimes with Cappi and the Hungarian gypsies. The gypsy band agreed to play for the wedding, playing the second day of the celebration free. When one of Gertrude's neighbors wondered why the "untouchables" were so welcome in Scheindorf and why Stefan was so friendly to them, Gertrude finally broke her silence and told the neighbor about the kindness of the Roma and the wagon ride many years ago.

"They're just like us," she said. "They have families and children. They struggle to feed their families. They sing and dance. They just live differently than we do!"

The story spread like wildfire in the village.

Maria worked on her dress and veil and helped the other women prepare the church, decorate the barn, prepare the house, and make the food. Then, as young women do, she argued with her mother about where the married couple would live.

"Of course you and Stefan will live here!" Frau Ditzig's frustrated voice reached Stefan where he stood on the porch ready to come in for Sunday supper. "You are much too young to live in a stranger's house. You will need your mother—for many things."

"Mother," Maria said patiently, "Stefan wants to live with his parents. The Revaks are hardly strangers. We've known them forever."

Stefan knocked on the door and overheard Maria say, "Besides, Mother, we'll be just right down the street."

Maria opened the door and smiled at Stefan.

"We have some things to work out, Mother and I," she whispered. "I'm sure the first of many."

He leaned over and kissed her. "I understand," he whispered. "I'll go and try to cheer her up."

Maria's heart raced as she waited for her father to knock on her bedroom door. She opened the window to take a few breaths of the fresh air, hoping to steady her heart. The lace curtains blew in with the cold wind that held a hint of the coming winter. The sky was ice blue with a few puffy clouds. There was frost on the grass and the nearby rooftops.

She could hear the excited conversations outside in the hall and downstairs. Stefan would be there, as would his parents, his Uncle Anton, and his mother's brother Johan, who lived in a nearby village, along with others. She walked over to the mirror and looked into her hazel eyes that danced with flecks of gold. Today would forever change the course of her life.

The white lace of her veil made her face paler than usual. She leaned in close to the mirror and gently pinched her cheeks to give them a little color. She adjusted her wedding crown made of fine wire, white trailing ribbons, and small pearls. Then she smoothed down the front of her three-quarter-length white wedding dress, adjusted the dark braids wrapped around her head, swept her veil across her shoulders, and stood tall. She was ready.

The knock came.

"Maria, are you ready?"

Maria walked to the door and opened it. She stood in the doorway a moment to capture the scene forever in her memory. The room was full of family—all waiting for her. Suddenly she was anxious. Then she saw Stefan, tall and handsome in his father's dark wool suit. He looked at her with such love she thought her heart would break, and her eyes instantly filled with tears. She reached out her hand to him, and he took it and kissed it. His hand was warm and strong. She smiled at him, looked in his dark eyes, and felt peace.

"You look so beautiful, Schatzi," he said.

It felt so right. Then she looked around the room, smiled, and silently thanked everyone for being there during this quiet moment of prayer before their marriage. She hardly noticed her mother fussing with her dress and the veil, tears slipping from her eyes.

Her small hand still in Stefan's hand, her father led the cluster of family through prayers: three Our Fathers followed by the Apostle's Creed. She looked up at Stefan. It was time to go to church.

Someone opened the door to the house, and the cold November wind gusted in, blowing the curtains and chilling the warm room. Maria and her father were the first out the door for the walk to St. Anne's Church. Since Stefan did not have a sister, the traditional partner of the groom on the walk to the church, Stefan walked with his mother and father, followed by their other family and friends.

Maria stayed close to her father, he rubbing her hand to keep hers warm, she holding on to the long veil that, buffeted by the wind, whipped around her. She turned around once to look at Stefan, who was talking with his mother, patting her hand on his arm. He looked up at her and smiled as if she were the only person in the world.

The church bells rang, heralding the procession, and people came out of their homes to watch or join in the parade. Children ran ahead, opening the doors of the church for the bridal party. Then they huddled in the back, giggling, waiting for everyone to enter, and thinking they had a secret. Yet everyone knew they would lock the church doors and people would have to pay to get out, as generations of children had done before them.

Inside the church, the altar was beautiful, simply decorated with the few remaining flowers of the fall season—a few sunflowers, colorful leaves, ribbons of green and gold, colorful gourds, grasses and fragrant dried herbs, and white candles that flickered in the relative darkness of the church. Herr Martin Gyetko played "Ave Maria" softly on the pipe organ while the wedding party assembled and the pews filled with parishioners. Finally, Father Ettinger appeared on the altar, his brocade ivory vestments a symbol of the sanctity of the sacrament about to take place.

Maria's head was spinning, but she found herself guided down the aisle by her father, hearing the pipe organ play one of her favorite preludes. Soon Stefan appeared and took her hand. They faced Father Ettinger, and their life together began.

Stefan and Maria were the first out of the church. They walked down the street, alone for a moment. The others would soon follow, after they negotiated payment with the children who guarded the doors.

"Have I told you how beautiful you look, my wife?" Stefan said. His heart was so full of happiness he felt it would burst.

"Only about ten times, my husband," Maria said, smiling.

He leaned down to kiss her.

"Are you cold?" he asked. "Let me give you my coat."

"I feel nothing but pure joy!" she said. "I'll be fine."

Nonetheless, he wrapped his arm around her shoulders, and they walked to the judge's barn for the grand noon communal meal. They were silent for those few moments, each with their own thoughts. This would be the only time they would be alone for some time. Except for a few hours of rest, the celebration of music, dancing, and food would go on for nearly three days as the community celebrated the beginning of their married life. Then it would be back to work.

CHAPTER ELEVEN

"It's not just the making of babies,
but the making of mothers
that midwives see as the miracle of birth."
Barbara Katz Rothman

Scheindorf
1938

STEFAN AND MARIA fell into the rhythm of life on the Revak farm and properties. Maria worked hard alongside her husband and his parents, doing her share of the housework, cooking, and chores on the farm. Gertrude taught her how to make some of the family favorites, like sausage and potato soup. Maria would simmer the smoked sausage with potatoes in water until the potatoes were fork-tender and the sausage had richly seasoned the soup. They would sip the savory meat broth, then mash the potatoes with a fork, and eat the sausage. He loved it!

On days when they worked together in the fields, Maria would pack a lunch of bread, hard cheese, a hunk of sausage, and apples, often sneaking in a piece of poppy seed and apple coffeecake. They would take their break together and talk. It gave them the private time they craved. Every day that went by, Stefan fell more deeply in love with his wife. She was his companion in all things, she was intelligent and beautiful, and she soothed his worries and supported his ambition.

Stefan was happier than he had ever been. He had waited years for Maria. She was finally his. Yet on the edge of his new life, worry was always a shadow.

Maria was pregnant. His emotions ran from thrilled that they were having a baby to terrified that something could go wrong. From discussions overheard in the wine cellar, he knew that in 1937, nine newly born babies had died in Scheindorf. Some of them had lost their mothers. Thinking about losing the love of his life in childbirth was unbearable.

Pregnant Maria worked as hard as anyone did. Every night she would kneel by their bed and pray the rosary for her baby's safe passage into the world.

One morning as they walked to the barn to water the horses, Maria said, "So what shall we name our baby?"

Stefan wrapped his arm around her shoulders and squeezed. "Well, I think we should stay away from Josef, Stefan, and Johan."

Maria laughed. "Because practically every man in town is named Josef, Stefan, or Johan?"

They laughed together.

"And don't forget girls' names—Magdalena, Rosalia, and Theresia. I think almost every girl has those names!" said Maria.

Stefan stopped and turned to her. "I think our child should have a special name—don't you?" He leaned over to kiss her smiling lips.

"Agreed," she said and looked into his eyes. His heart melted. She was even more beautiful pregnant. He would keep her safe—forever.

———•◦•———

It was still dark when Maria woke up. She was cramping. She put her hands on her rounded belly and suddenly felt it go tight. Her back ached. Was the baby coming?

She waited. Her mother had told her the pains would have to be regular before she was really in labor. She'd had contractions on and off for the past few days, but they always stopped. Would these?

Stefan slept next to her, his breathing regular.

She wanted to let him rest, but she was frightened. She felt alone. Could she do this? Would the baby be all right? Worries buried deep in the back of her mind suddenly surfaced in the dark of night. The stories she had heard of women who died in childbirth frightened her.

The pain came again—suddenly sharper. Then it went away as quickly as it had come. It was difficult, but Maria rolled over on her side, facing Stefan. She waited. *Nothing.*

She closed her eyes to rest. She had fallen asleep holding her rosary, and she fingered the beads, hoping the repetition of Hail Marys would put her back to sleep.

The pain returned swiftly, wrapped around her back, and squeezed hard. It left her breathless. This time, it lasted longer. Then as quickly as it came, it was gone.

"Stefan, Stefan," she whispered, shaking him gently.

He woke up startled.

"I think the baby is coming."

———•—•———

Frau Maria Ditzig watched her daughter stoically manage the pain of labor. When Gertrude alerted her, she had quickly dressed, grabbed the new baby blanket she had knit, and snatched up some clean but old pieces of cloth. She had rushed to her daughter's side before dawn. It was hard to watch her daughter suffer. Maria's face was covered in sweat, and she twisted the bedsheet in her hands, cold one moment, then hot the next, throwing them off.

It was now late afternoon. Frau Ditzig hoped the baby would come soon. Yet she knew that was not likely with a first birth.

"Another contraction is coming."

Maria squeezed so tight that Frau Ditzig felt she might crush her fingers or break her hand. Hours and hours had gone by, and still no baby. She had walked with Maria, as the midwife told them to do, until Maria could walk no more. Now she could do little but wait and pray. She wished she could trade places with her daughter.

Though she did not say it, Frau Ditzig was anxious. She had already lost her youngest, Mathilda. Her grief over that loss was both a feeling of emptiness and a constant, throbbing ache in her heart. She could not bear to lose her only living daughter or the baby—their first grandchild.

Ina May, the village midwife, her curly gray hair tied back with a piece of black cloth, sat calmly and watched. Nature would do most of the work. Gertrude ran in and out with cold cloths for Maria's forehead.

"How is Stefan?" Maria asked between contractions.

"Pacing. He won't sit down. He has been outside the door the whole time," Gertrude said. Her expression softened. "He won't leave you." She wiped the sweat tenderly from Maria's exhausted face.

After nearly fifteen hours of labor, Maria felt the uncontrollable urge to push. The contractions were coming one on top of the other.

"Push, Maria, push!" Ina May said. "Push with the contraction!"

Maria pushed with all her strength.

"I see the baby's head. She's crowning. Push again, Maria."

"I'm getting tired," Maria said, but she pushed again.

"You're almost there," Ina May said with a smile. "The head is out now. Gently push and we'll get the rest of this baby born."

As Maria obeyed, the midwife guided the baby into the world. She held up the newborn, slippery and covered with a white, creamy film.

The baby cried. They heard voices outside the door.

"It's a girl," Ina May whispered to Maria.

She showed Maria the ten fingers and toes—all looked well. Maria reached for her daughter. The baby looked at her mother through big, dark, glassy eyes.

Frau Ditzig's heart filled with the euphoria of witnessing the miracle of new life. Overwhelmed with emotion and relief, tears spilled from her eyes.

"She's bleeding," the midwife said to the grandmothers. "A little more than I'd like." Ina May gently but firmly massaged Maria's womb, hoping to slow the bleeding.

"Oh," Maria said. "That hurts." She grimaced and looked up at her mother, questioning.

Frau Ditzig's heart suddenly fell with worry. But she would not show it.

"It will be all right," her mother said. "Your womb must tighten to stop the bleeding. Feel it, now." She put Maria's hand on her abdomen with her own. "See, it is hard now. Every once in a while, gently massage it. It is normal to be tender."

Mothers could die quickly after childbirth from bleeding too much. The danger was not over. But she did not want Maria to see in her eyes the worry she felt.

"Let's see if the little one isn't too tired from her journey," Ina May said. She wiped the baby's face clean, clearing the nose and mouth. "We're going to try another midwife trick to stop the bleeding. Baby can help mother." She nestled the baby close to Maria's breast. "Maria, if she can nurse, that will also help tighten your womb."

Frau Ditzig nodded and helped to tuck the newborn close to Maria.

After a few minutes, Ina May said, "The blood flow is slowing down now." She took a wet cloth from Gertrude and washed Maria's face. "You did very well," she said with a smile. "You are a strong young woman."

Maria's mother breathed a sigh of relief. "May I hold the baby?" she asked tentatively. She looked at Ina May for approval. "Is it safe now?"

Ina May nodded.

"Yes," Maria said with a faint laugh. "Her name is Klothilde."

Tears of relief and happiness filled Frau Ditzig's eyes as she reached for her first grandchild. "Klothilde," she repeated. "She's beautiful!" She thought her heart would burst with love. She stared at the baby for a long time. "She looks like you, Maria."

"I see Stefan in her too," Gertrude said, looking over her shoulder.

"Can I show her to her father?" Frau Ditzig said.

Maria closed her eyes with a smile. "Of course. He must see her. He will be worried."

Frau Ditzig held the tightly wrapped baby, went to the door, and opened it. She nearly ran into Stefan, who stood there waiting. He looked exhausted. She looked into his eyes and saw his desperate love for Maria. It touched her profoundly. She'd always known he loved her daughter, but she had never seen the depth of his love until this very moment.

"Is she all right?"

Frau Ditzig smiled. Her heart warmed for him.

"She's going to be fine," Frau Ditzig said. "She's tired, and she will be for a while."

"The baby?"

Oma Ditzig held out the baby, smiled at him, and said, "It's a girl. God has blessed you and Maria. God has blessed us all."

CHAPTER TWELVE

"People are always blaming their circumstances for what
they are. I don't believe in circumstances.
The people who get on in the world are the people who get
up and look for the circumstances they want, and
if they can't find them, they make them."
George Bernard Shaw

Scheindorf
1939

THE WEISS STORE in Scheindorf was not only the place to shop but the hub of local gossip and the epicenter of news about the dramatic events, led by Adolf Hitler, that were unfolding not only in Germany but in Austria and now Poland. People came from all around to buy at the shop, bringing news of Germany's annexation of Austria, the anti-Slavic attitude of the German army, and the rumors of discrimination against Jews and others. Though many did not believe the stories, Herr Weiss was concerned about the potential for war. He was wise, and he was getting older.

Herr Weiss asked Stefan, the new father, to meet with him one day and told him he wanted to sell his store. He had hoped that his daughter and her husband would someday take over, but they were not interested. He named a very reasonable price, but Stefan had no money. His father owned the farm, all the land and livestock, the schnapps haus, and a portion of the mill.

That night, as the Revak family sat around the candlelit table, finishing the dinner of fragrant rosemary chicken, with its skin brown and crisp from the cast-iron pan, roasted potatoes, and carrots, Stefan brought up the idea of buying the store.

"Herr Weiss wants to sell the store," he said.

His father took a sip of coffee, put down his cup, and leaned back in his chair. "Yes, I know that," he said. "He's concerned about the possibility of war."

"War here?" Gertrude said. "We're a peaceful country. I've heard the rumors too. I don't believe them." She dismissed the conversation with a wave of her hand.

"Denying the possibility does not mean it won't happen," the judge said, looking in his wife's eyes. His eyes shot bolts of anger. Gertrude was silent.

His words hung in the air.

"We should all be worried about war," the judge finished.

"That's not what he told me," Stefan said. "He is getting older and does not want to continue running the business. He told me that he hoped his daughter and her husband would take over. They're not interested. He talked to me about buying it," Stefan said. "What do you think?"

There was silence.

Stefan leaned toward his father, "I'm really interested, Pop," he said. "It would be a business that Maria and I could manage, something we could build. Something for our family."

Gertrude nodded. Maria kept listening.

"If there is war, then everything changes—everything. It sounds like a good idea—in principle," the judge said. "But how would you manage the work here and the store? You've got a lot to think through." His father took another sip of coffee and pushed his plate away.

"Stefan, I think it could be a good idea," his mother said. "It would be interesting to own a store."

His father glared at his mother. She did not notice.

"Where would you get the money?" his father asked.

"Well, Pop, I was hoping you might help. I could pay you back, as the store got successful. It would take us some time, but I know we could do it."

The judge pushed his chair back from the table. "Enough of this talk," he said. He walked outside. Gertrude followed him with her eyes, said nothing, and got up to clear the table.

Stefan looked at Maria. Their eyes met across the table. He shook his head.

———•◆•———

Stefan was so busy on the farm and working the many plots of land his father owned that he did not have much time to think about buying the store or how he would pay for it. He did not give up on the idea, and he talked about it as much as he could with his father. But the judge would not commit, or more often, he refused to talk about it at all.

Work on the properties was demanding. They owned pigs, feeding and caring for them until they were butchered. Then they made hams, bacon, liverwurst, bloodwurst, and other sausages. Each type of food took time to prepare. The bacon cured in salted water for six weeks and then hung in the smokehouse along with the hams and sausages for six to eight weeks. On top of that there was the farming itself. They had added new and different crops, including the poppies they grew for seeds, which they used to season coffeecakes, muffins, strudels, and dishes like sauerkraut and sausage.

Stefan was deeply in love with his wife and young daughter. He wanted more for them than the hard life of farming. Maria, at eighteen, continued to work in the house and on the farm, taking turns with her mother and Gertrude caring for Klothilde.

One day in early spring, the young family was sitting on a blanket in the shade of the one tree left standing in the vast field of wheat, eating the lunch Maria had prepared.

"I think we should buy the store," Stefan said. "I've been thinking about this for a long time. You know that. We'd still have the farm and properties, but the store would be ours. It would be our business to run. This is Mama's and Pop's." He gestured to the land. "We work on it, but it is not ours. I am nearly twenty-five years old, and I own nothing. We have no money of our own. It's time for us to look out for our family—not to be so dependent on Mama and Pop."

Maria nodded.

"It's not that I'm ungrateful," he said. "I just want more for us."

"I understand," Maria said. "And I agree. We should be more independent."

"It would be a stretch," Stefan said. "We would have

to divide our time between the farms and the store. Maybe hire some help when we can afford it. But I think it would be a good investment. The village will always need a store." He smiled. "Especially the one you and I will plan."

"What about war? Your father talks with many people. What will happen if there is war?"

"We don't know if or when that will happen," Stefan said. "I can't live my life worried about what might happen. We have to make decisions based on what we know. What is possible now. Right now, I think it's the right thing to do. It's a great opportunity for us."

While Stefan talked, his eyes followed Klothilde as the baby explored the boundaries of their picnic blanket. The baby reached out past the edge of the blanket and looked back at her mother, testing. Maria shook her head, "No, stay here." Klothilde smiled and started to crawl away. Maria reached out and pulled her back, holding her in her lap.

"I could help with arranging the store, maybe some displays to encourage people to buy? It could be fun. We'd be working inside—especially in the winter!" She laughed. "We could have merchandise and displays by season, depending on what people needed. We might even sell canned goods from the farm or local knitting and linen."

"That would really help us support the community," Stefan said.

The next day Stefan went the store to find Herr Weiss. He was determined to buy it. They agreed on a price for the inventory, furniture, and fixtures. On a handshake, they drew up all the papers so that the store would be in Stefan's name. But Stefan still did not have the money.

The next day, he went to the stable to find his father. This would be the financial start of his life—a business of his own. He had made a list of everything he would need to restock the store. He planned to go to Satu Mare and purchase supplies from Kaufman, the wholesaler.

His father was feeding hay to the livestock, a pitchfork in his hands.

"Pop, we need to talk. You know I want the Weiss store. You know I've wanted it for months. Well, I talked with Herr Weiss. We agreed on a price—a very fair price. We drew up the papers—ready to sign. You know I don't have any money. The time has come. Will you help me?"

His father turned around to face Stefan. His eyes flashed with outrage. "You did what?" he shouted. "Without talking with me first?"

Stefan pleaded, "Pop, we've talked about this—I thought you wanted this for me."

"I don't want to talk about it."

Stefan could not believe what he was hearing. They had talked about buying the store many times. True, his father had not agreed to finance this step, but Stefan had hoped he would agree when the time came.

"Pop, I need a chance to make a life for myself—for my family!"

Judge Revak's eyes went dark with anger, and he lunged at Stefan with the pitchfork. Stefan jumped back, stunned.

His father screamed, "How do you think we're going to take care of my land—the crops—the livestock— with you running a store? Who's going to do that? Who is going to work the land? You want to make me bankrupt!"

Stefan held out his hands. His heart was pounding, and images of his mother wielding a scythe against him and Uncle Anton all those years ago flashed through his mind. He hardly knew where to start. "Pop, put it down. I don't want to make you bankrupt. I thought we could talk about this. I thought you wanted this for me. I've worked all my life for you."

Judge Revak stood his ground. "You are only thinking of yourself," his father said.

Anger was starting to rise in Stefan too—anger and a sense of injustice that burned bright. "Pop, I have no money. I've worked for you all my life, and I still don't have any money—no land or anything!"

The pitchfork was shaking in his father's grip. He kept the weapon pointed at Stefan.

Stefan backed further away. He could not believe they were having this conversation with a pitchfork between them. The discussion, after years of hard work, without reward, created a rift in their relationship of deep bitterness and resentment.

Disappointed and angry, he said, "Keep your money. Do whatever you want with it. I'll find the money somewhere else."

Without another word, he turned around and left the barn. He had worked the farm as a boy while his father was in America, kept working on it as a young man, and given it every ounce of his time and energy. He had been loyal to his father and his mother. It was not his intention to leave the farm; he just wanted more for his family.

Stefan heard his father call out to him, but he did

not stop.

He went to find Maria. She was working in the kitchen garden on her knees, picking lettuce and string beans for their dinner. He helped her up. She brushed off her skirt and faced him.

"You're upset," she said. "What's wrong?"

He immediately launched into the story of his father's rage.

Her face mirrored his feelings. "I can't believe he threatened you! After everything you've done for him. You worked the farm while he was in America. He would not have what he has now without you!"

He watched her eyes go dark with anger. She rarely erupted like this.

"I'm afraid of what I'm going to say—when I see him," she said. "You have a right to your own life." She looked down. "I'm so disappointed in him. What will your mother think?"

"I don't know. But I can't worry about that."

"What are you going to do?"

"I know Uncle Anton doesn't have the money. He did enough for us while Pop was in America. I'm going to see Uncle Johan. Don't tell Mama or Pop—I don't want them to know."

"I understand," Maria said. "I won't say anything."

"And pray for me," he said. "That I find the right words with Uncle Johan."

Maria took his hand and said, "I will pray. I believe in you, Stefan. You can do anything you put your mind to do."

———————

Stefan walked the three kilometers to Uncle Johan's home, growing more determined with every step. He had learned a great deal about his father today. The conversation both plagued and pained him, but he made up his mind to move on.

After greeting his uncle, Stefan started to talk about his plan, but Uncle Johan raised his hand and stopped him.

"No, don't tell me. Wait. Let's go to the wine cellar. We can talk there."

Stefan wondered but did not object. He followed his uncle to the wine cellar and down the stairs into the cool, dim interior. Barrels of wine were stacked in neat rows along either side of the long, narrow room. Uncle Johan lit a lantern, looked around, and found a glass thief.

"I need to taste this one." He pointed to an oak barrel. He uncorked the barrel and inserted the thief, siphoning out the wine and then transferring it to a glass. He gave the glass to Stefan.

"Now one for me." Uncle Johan repeated the process and corked the barrel.

He motioned to a table and two chairs.

"Sit. It is more private here. Get your breath, have a drink and we'll talk."

Stefan nodded, took a few deep breaths to settle his heart and compose his words, and then toasted his uncle.

"*Zum wohl!*" he said and looked him in the eye. His uncle nodded.

Together they took a sip of wine.

"It's good," Stefan said.

"It's almost ready," his uncle said. "It won't hurt us to drink it." Smiling, his uncle took a drink and motioned for him to talk.

Stefan launched into his story about the store, how he had wanted to be his own business owner, and his father's response. He shared his disappointment but was careful not to share too much of his bitterness. He felt as though his building resentment was creating a chasm, and it would split the ground between him and his father a long time.

After a few more glasses and some more conversation his uncle said, "Let's go home."

Stefan followed him home, still unsure what was going to happen. They went inside the house, and Uncle Johan said, "Sit down. I'll be right back."

Stefan sat and waited.

When Uncle Johan returned, he put six thousand *lei* down on the table in front of Stefan.

"Here—it's yours."

Stefan could not believe it. He leaned forward, not daring to touch the money.

"What about the papers—so I can sign for it?" Stefan asked.

"No papers," Uncle Johan replied. "I trust you."

Stefan was stunned. "I'll pay you back as soon as I can," he said. They stood and shook hands.

Stefan could hardly wait to tell Maria. But on the way home, he made another decision: he would not share the good news with his parents.

———

"I'm going to Satu Mare today," Stefan announced the next morning at breakfast. "I need to take the team and wagon. Gábriel is coming along to help."

Without explaining more, he got up and headed toward the stable.

A little later, Gertrude showed up at the stable where Stefan and Gábriel, their Hungarian hired hand, were hitching the horses to the wagon.

"I'm coming along," Gertrude said.

"Why, Mama?" Stefan asked. He really was not sure he wanted her with them.

"There are some things your father wants me to do in town."

Stefan was confused, but he, his mother, and Gábriel made the trip to the city. Gertrude and her son talked quietly about the trip to Satu Mare and their adventures with the gypsies. They laughed together at the memories. Gertrude had turned her life around since her husband returned from America. She enjoyed caring for her grand-daughter while Maria worked with Stefan in the fields. Stefan was grateful for her support. Though he had chosen not to tell her about her brother's generous loan, he felt she was on his side. She would learn about it soon enough.

When they arrived, Stefan went directly to Kaufman's wholesale supply. Stefan pulled out his list, and Kaufman filled his order. Stefan paid for everything, carefully counting out the lei. Then he went to other stores to buy wine and whiskey, tools and machine parts, and paid for everything.

When the wagon was full, Gertrude said to Stefan, "I don't know why your father sent me here." She seemed confused.

"Mama, you told me you had something to buy," Stefan replied.

"No, no—your father sent me. He said that anything you needed, I should pay for."

Stefan caught his breath. Anger and bitterness burned in his chest. His father's attempt at generosity had come too late. He got off the wagon loaded with supplies, looked up at his mother, and said, "Mama, as you can see, I paid for all of this. I have money. I don't need Pop's." He shook his head. "I'm going to take the autobus home. I need time to think."

Judge Revak sat at home alone that night. It was quiet in the house. Klothilde was asleep in her bed. Maria, Stefan, and Gertrude had left to meet Gábriel. They were going to unload the wagon and start setting up the store. When they'd left the house, they were as excited as children anxious to play with a new Christmas toy.

Gertrude had told him that Stefan had paid for everything. She had also told him what Stefan had said. The judge felt left out—once again. He had missed four years of his son's life while he was in America. Now he had chosen, in his selfishness, to fail his son during one of the most important moments of his young life. His son was achieving one of his dreams, and he was doing it without his father's help. Even worse, he was doing it without his father's support. It was a missed opportunity. Stefan had worked hard on the farm from childhood and received no wages—not even a piece of property.

What had he done? He should have been proud of his son's ambition. Instead, he got angry with him for wanting a better life.

As a father, he had been self-centered—thinking only of himself.

He sat in the dark, and tears filled his eyes.

Between work on the farm, Stefan and Maria set up the store. It was hard work, but it was fun. It was something that belonged to them.

Maria was in the store arranging a colorful display of ribbons and cloth when the little bell over the door rang in greeting. She looked up to see her father-in-law in the doorway. It was his first visit. He had been quiet at home since they had bought the store, both he and Stefan distant, just saying what needed to be said to each other. She wondered how long it would take for one of them to relent. They were both stubborn. She knew that Stefan would forgive his father if only his father would reach out to him.

She walked over to him. "Hi, Pop, come on in."

He took off his hat, walked in, and looked around the store, looking surprisingly timid.

"Is Stefan here?"

"No, he had to take the wagon for an adjustment. He should be back soon," she said.

The judge walked around the store, picking up a new hand tool here and there, looking at their stack of empty ledgers on the counter, nodding at their progress. He did not say anything for a few minutes.

"You've done a lot of work. It looks good," he said.

"Thanks Pop. Yes, it has been hard work—but work

we do together. Besides, it is very important to Stefan."
Silence hung between them for a few minutes.

"I could help, sometimes, you know?" Judge Revak fingered the rim of his hat and looked down. "I'm good with business, and I know people—and if you and Stefan get busy I could help you with the store."

Maria smiled. She knew the store would meet the judge's need to be in the middle of everything. With his love of politics, world events, and conversation—he would be the first to know the latest news or stories. The store had been drawing the village and outlying communities in like a magnet. It would be the perfect stage for him.

She was glad he had come. He had taken the first step toward reconciliation.

Maria went over to him and gave him a hug. She felt him pull back in surprise. "Yes, Pop, we could really use your help. You are always welcome here."

They smiled at each other. A tear slid down his cheek, and he brushed it away.

She understood, and in her heart, she forgave him.

CHAPTER THIRTEEN

*"The two most important days in your life
are the day you are born and
the day you find out why."*
Mark Twain

Scheindorf, Romania/Hungary
1940–41

IN THE FALL of 1940, the Romanian army once again called Stefan for his annual two-week service in the reserves. Maria and Stefan had just discovered they were expecting. The store was busy, and the farm work, land management, and vineyards were all consuming. His infantry company was in training about a kilometer from the town, and their orders were to march another hundred kilometers further into Romania. Stefan was concerned about leaving his family. He was also concerned about what he might encounter on maneuvers. The volatility of war was rippling across Europe.

Torn between his duty to his country and his obligation to family, he left home to report for duty but decided to pay a visit to Major Krause, the head of his company, first. Krause was a far different man than his Baia Mare platoon leader, Major Schneider. He knew of Major Krause's love of food and drink. He walked to the company camp, bringing along several bottles of wine and whiskey, a gift for the major.

He found the corpulent major alone in his tent.

"Revak—you back again. Already?"

"Yes, I'm supposed to report today. But I came to see you first." Stefan put the bottles down on the table in front of the major. "I brought you some excellent wine and fine whiskey."

"Why, thank you!" Krause smiled and reached for the whiskey. "Sit down, sit down. I've always time for a drink or two." He pulled out a glass and poured himself a drink. He held up the bottle. "Some for you?"

Stefan shook his head and pulled up a camp chair near his commanding officer.

Krause took a sip of the dark liquor. "This is good. You made this?"

"Yes, we make whiskey, wine, and schnapps—from the best of our crops."

"Very good," the major said, looking at the bottle and refilling his drink.

They talked about family and farming for a few minutes. The major continued to drink.

"Stefan, you are so stupid," he said at last and put down his glass.

"Why? What do you mean?" Stefan asked.

"You're too busy farming to know." The major took another drink and added, "And making good whiskey." He laughed.

Stefan waited. He sensed there was more to the major's half-drunken admonition than he realized . . . something important. He was glad he had come.

The major leaned close to Stefan and said, "Ever heard of the Second Vienna Agreement?"

Stefan shook his head. He knew from what he had heard through the village grapevine and in the store, that Europe was vulnerable to Hitler's and Mussolini's ambitions. Borders were shifting and government leadership and power susceptible to change.

"I thought not," the major said. "It was signed on August 30." He paused to take another drink. "Countries and borders are political currency these days. The German Nazis and those Fascists from Italy negotiated the deal."

Stefan sat quietly and listened. He realized there was much he did not know about the events that surrounded his world.

"I'm not supposed to talk about this, but—in a few days, the Romanian army won't be here. You're from Scheindorf. Once again it will become part of Hungary." He laughed. "And here you are coming back now!" He raised his hands as if to question Stefan's sanity and shook his head.

Stefan thought for a minute or two as they exchanged toasts. *I can make as if I was never here,* he decided. The major was likely right, and he had no desire to be a part of the confusion and uncertainty in the military that would come with the politics of the change. He was needed at home.

"Go on, get out of here." The major waved his hand, dismissing him. "I never saw you."

Stefan got up. He kept his thoughts to himself, left the major drinking whiskey, and headed out of the tent, carefully avoiding contact with anyone who might know him.

He went to the train station. Instead of walking

home, where someone he knew might spot him, he planned to take a roundabout way on the train. He would hide in Scheindorf until Hungary took over.

He boarded the train, but his plan quickly backfired when he saw someone he knew. He got off the train before it reached Scheindorf and hid in the woods overnight. He walked through the fields toward home as dawn was breaking.

When Stefan walked into the house, his father was sitting at the kitchen table, nursing a cup of coffee, his head buried in a ledger. Preoccupied with his work, he did not notice Stefan.

"Hi, Pop."

The judge looked up, startled, and his eyes widened in shock. "Jesus Maria, what are you doing here?"

"It's okay, Pop. Scheindorf belongs to Hungary again. The Romanian army will be leaving soon."

"They can hunt you down and kill you as a deserter!" His father stood up.

"Calm down, Pop." Stefan held up both of his hands, pleading. "It will be all right. I've thought it through. I have a plan."

Maria walked into the kitchen. "I heard voices," she said. She raised her hand to her heart and stood still. "Stefan, what are you doing here?" Her brow furrowed, and her eyes burned with worry.

"I told him—he could be shot as a deserter!"

Stefan gave Maria a quick hug. Her body was unyielding and stiff.

"Let me explain." Quickly, he explained about the borders changing and the agreement signed in late August that would make Scheindorf Hungarian once again.

"That's all well and good," Maria said, "but what are

you going to do between now and then? Where will you hide? Klothilde—what will we tell her? How do you expect a three-year-old to keep a secret?"

"Hear me out," he said. "I've been thinking about this all night."

Maria looked at him and shook her head.

"I can stay in the barn. You and Mama can bring me food. I'll go out and work in the fields—no one will see me. But we'll need to make some sort of cover around the wagon so that I can't be seen when I drive the team out there." Maria put her hands on her hips and tilted her head in disbelief, but Stefan continued with his plan. "I'll work all day, get back in the wagon, drive to the barn, and later sneak into the house after dark to spend the night—it's that easy!" Stefan smiled at them, trying to engage them in his plot.

"It still frightens me, Stefan," Maria said and put her arms around him. "We have another child coming." She looked seriously into his eyes. "A child who needs a father."

"It will be all right, Schatzi," he soothed. "Try not to worry." He gave her a quick kiss. "I'll be careful. I promise."

"Stefan," his father said. "This is a dangerous game you play."

"I'll be careful, Pop. It won't be long."

Some weeks later, what Stefan predicted happened. The new Hungarian army came through the village.

When Stefan came out of hiding, the villagers were surprised at how quickly he had returned home.

———·◆·———

Though the winter of 1941 was long and cold, the transition to Hungarian rule had little impact but to change the individuals in government office. Stefan Revak Senior remained mayor. The unseen war around them intensified, and Scheindorf began to feel more and more of its impact. Stefan and Maria were not able to get all of the supplies for their store. Yet, insulated from the world events by lack of communication, distance, and the size of their village, most people in Scheindorf were blind to the war's dangerous progression.

Maria's baby grew as winter turned to spring and spring to summer.

On July 19, 1941, Maria and Stefan walked slowly to a field a few kilometers from home where they grew wheat. The day was warm, the sky bright blue. Nine months pregnant, Maria was still working. Cultivating wheat was hard, and everyone had to help. The judge and Gertrude had errands to do and took Klothilde with them. They would come out to the field later.

It was hot. Maria stopped to drink from the water jar.

"Oh," she said. She wrapped her arms around her lower belly and looked down.

A steady stream of warm, clear liquid was trickling down her leg, pooling in the chalky earth by her feet. Her back started to ache; then a contraction came so hard she felt she might faint.

"Stefan!" she called to him. "Stefan! The baby's coming!"

"We need to get you home," Stefan said.

She was worried. This was starting much more quickly than last time; the pains were much sharper. "Our baby can't be born in the field!" Maria pleaded. He nodded and wrapped an arm around her back so she could lean on him as they walked.

They headed for their house in the village. The labor pains got stronger with every step she took. She had to stop and rest several times along the way. The pain was intense. She focused hard on moving—getting to the house before the baby came. She found herself whispering, "Holy Maria, Mother of God, pray for us," repeatedly.

Stefan helped her, his arm wrapped around her, holding her up as she slowly walked. She could feel his anxiety.

When they finally made it home, it was about noon. Stefan went next door and sent his cousin, Rosalia, to get Ina May. He got back just in time. Maria, still in the kitchen, cried out, "Ohhhhhh!"

She had no control. The baby was coming! She dropped down on her hands and knees on the kitchen floor. She felt the baby slide out.

"Stefan, Stefan! The baby is here! The baby is here!" Maria reached down.

"I'll get help," he said and started to leave.

She turned to him. "No! Stay with me!"

Stefan went down on his knees by Maria. Kneeling on the floor, Maria took the baby girl, wrapped her in the folds of her skirt, and gently dried her off. Then she picked up the wiggling Siglinda and held her close to her chest. The baby was fussy, making little squeaks, crying occasionally.

Relief flooded her. She held the baby close, supporting the head, and looked at her. Siglinda had already found her fist and was sucking on it. She looked up at her mother with dark blue eyes.

"Look, Stefan, she's beautiful!" Maria said.

Within a few minutes, Rosalia appeared. Ina May was coming. Oma Ditzig was coming. Maria had their new daughter in her arms, checking her fingers and toes, talking to her.

"Stefan, take her for a minute," Maria said. She passed the baby to Stefan. Maria took a few deep breaths, leaning with her hands on her knees. A wave of exhaustion and dizziness hit her hard. The long walk and the turmoil of the birth had caught up with her. "I think I'm bleeding again."

She looked into his eyes and saw his love and concern.

"It will be all right. Ina May will be here soon," he said.

Maria laughed quietly. "Not much left to do," she said.

"Ina May will help stop the bleeding," Stefan said. "You will be fine. I won't let anything happen to you. Rest for a minute. I've got her."

"She's beautiful, isn't she?" Maria said, watching her daughter's tiny fingers curl around her father's finger.

"She's beautiful, just like her mother."

Maria looked into Stefan's eyes, and her heart melted.

During the remainder of 1941, the war escalated all around Scheindorf. The judge was privy to a steady stream of information from people who came through the village and from his political contacts. He learned of the advance of the German army into Russia and of the Russian partisans "scorched earth" tactics: set fire to the crops already harvested, drive away livestock, and destroy their buildings.

He was shocked and devastated when he learned that on December 7, 1941, the Japanese had bombed Pearl Harbor. His heart nearly stopped when on December 11, 1941, Germany declared war on the United States of America.

CHAPTER FOURTEEN

"In love we find out who we want to be;
In war, we find out who we are."
Kristin Hannah

Scheindorf, Hungary
February 1942

WHILE STEFAN CONDUCTED an inventory of supplies in the store, he watched the two German officers set up their workstation and open a large ledger on the table. They had come to register all men, from boys of thirteen to grandfathers of fifty-five, for potential service in the German army. Stefan overheard them talking.

"If only we had taken Moscow, we wouldn't need to do this."

"Every man should be honored to serve the Reich. The spring campaign is about to start. We need more men." The senior officer pointed to the ledger and said, "We need to collect their religion as well as age."

"Yes, sir."

Word of the war's progression first reached Scheindorf in whispers, then letters from relatives and visits from people passing through town. Stefan, acutely aware of the potential impact of the war, was deeply concerned when Germany declared war against the United States. His father believed this move was foolhardy and would be the end of Germany, as they knew it.

Scheindorf now felt the insidious impact of war. War no longer knocked on their door. It had entered their homes.

Some supplies were impossible to obtain. Two Hungarian soldiers were posted in the village to report and control resistance. Stefan's father told him that after Hungary took over Romanian territory, a grenade in Ip had killed four Hungarian soldiers. The attack resulted in the retaliatory killing of over one hundred villagers. Stefan heard more such stories as the war created chaos and spawned fear everywhere.

After all this time, war had reached Scheindorf almost overnight. Their life had turned from safe and secure to uncertain and vulnerable.

Maria moved away from the soldiers and walked over to Stefan. Her look was serious and direct. They had talked earlier about the possibility of Stefan being called to duty and what they should do. It was time to make some key decisions. It was not going to be easy for either of them.

"Come with me," he said.

They walked into the storeroom. He shut the door. They compared notes about what they had overheard.

"We need to prepare for the fact that this *is* going to happen. I *will* be called to duty. I'm an experienced soldier."

"We don't live in Germany. Why are they here?"

"We are in a world war. Hungary has joined the Axis Powers. The search for men to fight as soldiers is much greater than just Germany. Germany's losses have been great. We should be thankful that I'm young and strong enough to survive."

"I guess we should be grateful that we don't have a thirteen-year-old son who could be called to serve," Maria said bitterly.

Stefan nodded.

"What if you have to fight Americans? What will you do?"

"I don't believe in this war any more than you do. The deportation of Hungarian Jews by the Nazis makes no sense. Declaring war on America is suicide for Germany. I'm sure there are many things going on that if we knew them would frighten us even more. But someone has to protect the villages and our cities. Scheindorf could someday be at risk if, let's say, the Russians make it here. Who will protect us if not our army?" Stefan kept the depth of his fear to himself. Maria was already anxious.

He sighed. "I don't have all the answers. I can only hope and pray that I won't have to fight Americans or have anything to do with harming defenseless people. I need you to pray for this. Not just for my safety, but that I don't have to get any dirtier than war already is."

Stefan reached out and took Maria in his arms. He felt her lean into him, and he stroked her hair. His cheek rested on her hair, and he smelled the fresh, clean scent. He loved her so much. Everything about her.

"I will pray," she said. "Every day, every night."

"We can do this," he murmured. "It probably won't be for more than a year."

They were both silent for a moment.

He held Maria at arm's length and looked deeply

into her eyes. The joy he used to see shining there had darkened to fear.

"We'll have to do this day by day. I don't know what the future will bring."

"That is probably a good thing," Maria said.

He nodded.

"We need to sell the store. Mr. Baumgartner will buy it. When I get back, we'll open another business."

Maria nodded, listening, but her eyes filled with tears.

He faced her and wiped away the few tears that had spilled from her eyes. "We can do this, you and I. You are stronger than anyone I know. Now let's get out there and get this over with. And never let them know how we feel."

Maria nodded. She took out a handkerchief and blew her nose. She smiled at him, and they walked out together to face a future they had never planned to meet.

PART III

CHAPTER FIFTEEN

*"Never think that war, no matter how necessary,
nor how justified, is not a crime."*
Ernest Hemingway

Austria, Belarus, Russia, Poland
1942–43

ON MARCH 27, 1942, Stefan, inducted into the German army with Maria's father and other men from Scheindorf and the surrounding communities, traveled via train to Vienna and the Army Replacement and Training Division, Military District 17. Vienna had been under Austrian rule until 1938, when Hitler, a native Austrian, contrived the *Anschluss* (union) with Germany.

Stefan moved in a line with hundreds of nameless men waiting to be processed. Like the others, he wore black army-issue underwear. The number 349 hung around his neck. Though it had just been a few days, he felt as if he had been away a lifetime. While he waited he wondered what was happening back home. It was late winter, time for making lye soap, taking inventory, and planning for spring crops.

He thought of each member of his family, missing

them, but finally found a reason to smile—the memory of Klothilde's mysterious obsession with eating coal. They did not know what she was doing, at first. They just saw the mysterious ring of black around her mouth and wondered why. Later, when they found out she was eating coal, Maria was worried. But the doctor had told them it was normal for a child, like a pregnant woman, to crave unusual things. As long as she was not hurt, it was okay. Thankfully, Klothilde outgrew it.

The line was moving. At one station, an army doctor wearing a white coat listened to Stefan's heart and lungs and nodded. At the next station, a dentist checked his teeth. The third station was a check for vision. At the fourth station, his blood type was determined. Pronounced fit to serve, Stefan sat down in a chair in front of a barber, who, surrounded by a small mountain of multi-colored hair, quickly shaved his head.

Stefan's uniform consisted of a standard dark green, six-button field tunic, trousers, anklets, and ankle boots. His buttoned flap cap, embroidered with an eagle insignia, matched the eagle on his uniform's right pocket. An olive-drab steel helmet, bayonet, and entrenching shovel completed his gear.

After an interview about his military service, Stefan was awarded the rank of corporal. He was assigned to the First Infantry Group of the German 4th Army with three other friends from Scheindorf: Franz Moore, Martin Schimpf, and Stefan Müntz. The others reported to other divisions. Stefan felt fortunate to have a few friends in his group.

Each of the men was issued a *Wehrpass*, a military service record book about the size of a passport, and the *Soldbuch*, or pay book, containing the soldier's registration number, medical history, and rank promotions. Around their necks hung metal identity disks, to be worn at all times, engraved with their registration number and blood type. While they were in uniform, transportation by train was free.

With his friends from Scheindorf and other soldiers, Stefan was ordered to report to German-occupied Babruysk in Belarus for basic training. They boarded the night train to Warsaw; from there they would travel through Minsk to Babruysk. They were able to snag seats in the same area. They would be sitting up all night.

Stefan Müntz and Franz dozed off. Two German Nazi party officers entered the car and sat behind Stefan and Martin. On edge, he found it impossible to sleep. He listened to their conversation.

"How is your wife?"

"Safely tucked away in the *schloss*. I moved her from Berlin months and months ago. I have not seen her for some time. Her mother is with her."

"That was a good to get her out of the city."

"*Ja, ja*, a very good move."

He heard one of the officers sigh.

"How are things going?"

"In Babruysk?"

"Nearly cleansed of the vermin."

Even with the officer's voice a whisper, Stefan could hear his loathing.

Stefan glanced over at Martin. He was asleep.

"When did we first occupy them?"

"June 28 last year."

"So, what are the figures?"

The officer lowered his voice.

"I understand some twenty thousand Jews, some

Roma . . . at first we deported them; then it became easier not to transport."

"Hmm, shot the mice? Gassed them?"

"Keep your voice down!"

"Why? We should be proud!"

Stefan heard the arrogance in the faceless voices. Blood pounded in his ears.

He did not hear the response.

The callous conversation shook Stefan to the core. He served in the same army as the Nazi officers. He had Jewish and Romani friends. He thought of Cappi, and of the Jewish shopkeeper in New York who had lent his father money to bring his family to America. He thought of the Hungarian gypsies who played music for days at his wedding. He thought of them, and he kept his eyes closed, and burned with anger at this war and ached with longing for home.

———◆·◆———

When they reached Babruysk, though many of the businesses were shuttered closed, they smelled food and found an open café. The long trip had left them hungry and tired. The short menu was written in Russian on a black chalkboard. They had no clue what it said.

The four men found a booth in the back and ordered soup and bread by pointing to the food other customers were eating. The lean, elderly Belarusian woman who took their order eyed them with disdain.

"*Haben sie Kaffee?*" Franz asked.

The woman looked at him and raised an eyebrow.

"I don't think she speaks German, Franz," Stefan said.

"Chai?" she said.

"Is that coffee?" Franz asked his friends.

"I don't know," Martin said, "I don't speak Russian!"

"Chai," Stefan said to the woman.

No one said anything for a while, uncertain what to say. They were German army soldiers in Belarus. They were the enemy. It felt uncomfortable.

When their food arrived, Stefan was starving, so he dove in. The watery soup was pale pink with beets and bits of cabbage, but it was hot and soothing. He dipped the dry, days-old black bread in the soup and ate every bite. The "coffee" was not coffee; it was black tea. There was no sugar, but there was powdered milk. He stirred it into his mug and sipped the warm tea from the chipped white cup.

"I hope she didn't spit in my soup," Franz said as he looked down into his bowl. He had yet to take a bite.

Stefan shook his head. "Better eat." He motioned to Franz's soup. "We don't know what's next. And we've got to report to duty today."

"They need the business to stay alive," Martin said. "The soup's fine."

"We'd feel the same way, if we were occupied," said Stefan Müntz.

"Yes, how would you feel if the Russian army invaded Scheindorf?"

Stefan looked around. There was no one near to overhear them.

"They've been through a lot, these people," he said. "People have left the city—their homes and businesses." He paused, trying to find the words. "Did you hear the officers talking on the train to Warsaw?" The others shook their heads. "The Jews here have been murdered—

thousands of them. Gypsies too."

Saying it aloud made the atrocity come to life.

"I knew we'd heard rumors, but here?" Martin said. "Germany did this?"

Stefan nodded.

There was silence for a few minutes. No one knew what to say.

"This is not going to be any fun," Franz said.

"When did you figure that out?" Stefan said.

———————

The four friends went to the public library to report for duty. Most of the city's municipal buildings had been converted into army service after the 1941 German invasion, and the library swarmed with men typing orders, filing papers, and delivering documents. At a reception desk, Stefan asked to see Captain Eichelberger. Without looking up from the stack of papers piled on his desk, a corporal held out his hand and said, "Your orders."

After reading the document, the corporal sent the four Scheindorf men to another desk where a different corporal stamped the orders.

"Take this to the building next door. It is yellow brick with a red tile roof. Ask for Senior Lance Corporal Hirsch."

On the second floor of the yellow-brick building, Stefan found Nevin Hirsch, an intense, unsmiling man with deep-set eyes. Wearing an Iron Cross awarded for bravery in battle, he wasted no time launching into their orders.

"The Russians are fanatics and animals," he said.

"When we overran the Russian lines, small bands of enemy soldiers escaped. They know the country. They hide out in the forest, and the villagers are sympathetic to their cause. They have joined with them against Germany."

He paused and looked Stefan directly in the eyes. "There is now an underground army behind our lines. They're well-armed, well-fed, and supported by the Americans and the British."

Hearing the word "Americans," Stefan took a deep breath. He was caught in the crossfire of a war he had not chosen.

Hirsch went on. "They blow up railroad bridges, tear up the track, cut communication lines, and ambush our convoys. They burn crops and kill livestock. They must be stopped. Corporal Revak, you and your men are now a machine-gun team charged with killing Russian sympathizers—army and civilian."

Stefan could not sleep that night. All his father and mother had talked since he was a little boy was about was America—going to America—beginning a new life there. How many hours had they spent talking of how America was a wonderful country? Here he was supposed to fight in a war against America, in a war that killed Jews, a war that murdered civilians who fought to protect their country. What was he doing here?

What was happening to his family? Who would protect them? Would they become a casualty of war like so many others?

———

On the gun range, Stefan listened intently as Corporal Hirsch introduced the men to the *Maschinengewehr 34.* This was a fight to live. Stefan wanted to live.

"The MG 34 is a general-purpose, air-cooled machine gun able to fire up to nine hundred rounds a minute," said Hirsch. "Mounted on its tripod, the gun is fed Mauser cartridges loaded inside ammunition belts. A belt contains fifty rounds. Link the belts together for sustained fire. If you are using several belts at a time, the gun barrel gets hot and can misfire, so you need to change barrels. Gunners, when you change barrels, you need to wear an asbestos glove. You will carry three backup barrels and ammunition boxes. Each box holds five belts."

Demonstrating the MG 34, Hirsch taught the new team procedures to change barrels in a matter of seconds.

"You need at least two men to operate the MG 34. One fires and the other feeds ammunition and changes barrels. Your team leader spots the gun and provides protection."

Turning to Stefan, he said, "As team leader, you'll carry an MP 40 submachine gun."

Four days after arriving in Babruysk and training with Hirsch, the team was thrust into the field.

———•—•———

Stefan and his MG 34 team were in position, concealed behind rocks on a wooded hill overlooking a quiet village in Belarus. He watched as other MG 34 teams took their places surrounding the village. He scanned the surrounding area for movement. There was no activity in the village streets. He could not help but think of Scheindorf as he looked down on the peaceful setting.

"We're their cover fire," he whispered to his team. Within two weeks of leaving home for Vienna, Stefan was preparing to fight not the Red Army, but civilians. With his MP 40 *Maschinenpistole* armed and ready, he watched the German troops move from house to house, kicking in doors, searching for Russian sympathizers, guns, and explosives.

Beside him, Stefan Müntz pointed and said, "Stefan, look—the town's on fire!"

Smoke was billowing from one of the roofs. In less than thirty minutes, the village was consumed by fire. A column of German infantry soldiers walked down the road out of the village. Tied to the belts of several soldiers were slaughtered chickens and ducks, hanging by their necks.

A sergeant approached Stefan's position on the hill.

"Pack it up," he ordered. "Found some weapons. No one home."

For the next six weeks, Stefan and his unit hunted Russian partisans, moving from village to village, burning homes, and other buildings. During those six weeks, Stefan heard they had captured two men, but he never saw them. There was no shortage of food. It was mostly army food, but occasionally they would find a pig or a cow to butcher for fresh meat. He tried not to think of the impact on the farmers and families. It was a wet and cold early spring in Russia, and sleeping on the frozen ground made the nights long and uncomfortable.

During one raid, they captured some fifty Clydesdale horses from a horse farm. Constantly on the move, not knowing the terrain or even their location on a map, made the going difficult. The horses, loaded with their supplies, were a huge asset—and to Stefan, they felt like old friends.

One clear and cold starry night in early May, Stefan's unit wove their way through a forest searching for a bridge where they could cross the river. When Stefan reached it, he could hardly believe his eyes. It was little more than wood planks nailed together—hardly a crossing for horses. Nevertheless, they had no choice. They had to try.

The first horse in line was skittish, frightened by the noise of the river. No matter how Stefan pulled or pushed, the horse would not move. Stefan hooded the Clydesdale with a blanket to calm him. Speaking to the horse in soothing tones, he led him to the bridge. The sound of the rushing river, just a couple of feet below them, was deafening. The horse took a few slow steps on the rickety bridge. Suddenly, one of the boards gave way. The horse's right front leg broke through the board. The gelding screamed in pain, lost his balance, and fell over into the water.

Stefan and Franz quickly shed their packs and coats and jumped into the freezing water to rescue the horse and their equipment. While Franz worked to recover their gear, Stefan swam to the horse. Wide-eyed with fear, the gelding tossed his head, his eyes rolling back in pain, struggling to swim in the churning water. The horse was drowning. Stefan, swimming alongside, tried to lead the horse to a shallow place where he could stand. He was exhausted, his body going numb from the cold. Stefan finally found a place to stand in the riverbed, but the horse could not. He had broken his leg.

Stefan trudged out of the water, found his MP 40 where he had left it, and walked to the middle of the bridge. The horse still fought to stand in the riverbed. Stefan knew what he had to do, and though he dreaded it, he would do it quickly. He aimed his MP 40 at the horse's head and pulled the trigger. The horse dropped into the water and soon disappeared.

Stefan took a deep breath and walked back to solid ground.

"We need to move," he said. "If there are partisans in the area, they heard the gunshots."

One by one, they hooded the remaining eight horses and safely crossed the bridge. The soldiers continued their trek toward the Russian front following the road. The road opened into a small clearing, and Stefan, in the lead, walked right into a hail of bullets. A bullet hit him and ripped through his large winter coat, narrowly missing his body. His heart pounded.

"Retreat! Retreat!" Stefan ordered. "They're in the trees!"

Stefan took cover behind one of the horses that was down—killed by sniper shots. With his MP 40, he lay down a barrage of cover fire. Schimpf and Müntz ran out with the MP 34, quickly deployed the tripod, and shredded the trees on the far side of the clearing with bullets.

Stefan dropped back into the woods, and using hand signals, divided the squad into two teams, assigning one man to stay with the horses.

"Fan out! Watch the flanks."

Heading back to the clearing, Stefan called Franz to his side. While Franz ran to him, Stefan provided cover fire for his friend.

"Follow me," Stefan said.

While the firefight continued, the two men worked their way around the clearing, staying concealed in the forest, and approached the sniper's nest from the rear. Two snipers were shooting from the trees, and two had taken cover behind large logs.

Stefan quickly silenced any conversation with a finger to his lips and then pointed to the two in the trees. Franz nodded.

Stefan pulled out a grenade and lofted it into the trees as Franz shot. It exploded. One shooter dropped, then the second. Quickly, he pulled the pin and threw another grenade. It flashed and boomed, wounding the men on the ground.

The forest fell silent.

They walked over to the fallen partisans. Stefan checked for pulses. Three were dead. He walked over to the fourth body and turned it over to feel for a pulse. The sniper was a woman. Long brown curly hair had slipped from her hat, and her dark eyes showed surprise in death.

They had killed a woman—a woman protecting her country. Stefan thought of Maria. He felt the knife of fear slice through his heart as he realized another sobering reality of war. How many more were there to discover?

On June 28, 1942, Germany began another massive offensive against Russia, the *Fall Blau*. Most of the troops knew little of the status of the war. They showed up and did what they were told, walking or being trucked from one location to another. The Russian steppes were blazing hot, the roads were dusty, and there was not a tree in sight. Stefan lost track of the days and weeks as they all blurred together. They fought through July. He must have missed Siglinda's birthday. He was lonely, tired, and often lost in the vast land of Russia.

One day Stefan overheard two officers talking, pointing at a map.

"We'll attack from this direction."

Within days, all of a sudden they were at the front, a few miles from Stalingrad. They were in the thick of battle. Combat was man-to-man, the Russian military tactic of "hugging," keeping the enemy close so they could not be aided by air support. Russian soldiers were so close they threw hand grenades at the Germans. The machine gunfire was deafening. The heavy smoke burned Stefan's lungs. He could hardly see. Within minutes, a bullet to the chest hit Stefan Müntz. Cursing his luck, he was quickly pulled to safety by his friends.

Stefan was in a fight for his life. Men all around him were falling, either wounded or killed in the hail of bullets, the explosion of grenades, and the vicious rain of shrapnel. Stefan fired his machine gun with a vengeance he had never felt before, strafing the unseen enemy with a fierce hail of bullets. He was not fighting for Germany. He was fighting to live. He would see Maria again. He would see his daughters. The war would not separate him from those he loved most. He would survive.

A grenade flew through the air toward Stefan. It hit his gun and detonated. The sound echoed in his ears, and his head pounded from the force of the explosion. He was stunned by the blast. He shook it off and tried to shoot. Nothing. His finger would not work. He looked at his hand. His trigger finger hung loose, attached by a thread of tissue. Blood streamed from his hand. The pain burned like his hand was on fire. He felt light-headed, then he saw blackness and pinpoints of light, and he dropped to his knees.

"Medic! Medic!" someone called.

That was all Stefan remembered until he woke up in the tent that served as the field hospital. He was lifted onto a set of wooden planks that passed for an operating table. A nurse slipped a thin piece of wood between his teeth and told him to bite down. While several soldiers held him down, a doctor, without any drugs for pain or anesthesia, amputated his finger. His teeth clamped down on the wood, and tears streamed down the side of his face. The pain was excruciating, and even after they bandaged his hand, he could still feel his finger, no longer there, throbbing with pain. Stefan squeezed his eyes closed and hoped desperately that his injury would be the end of his days as a soldier.

After several weeks in the hospital, Stefan was announced fit for duty. It made no sense. He could not pull a trigger. How could he fight? But the army had other ideas. Stefan's new job was more dangerous than fighting. He was carrying ammunition, unarmed, to the gunners in foxholes. He realized that every man, regardless of age or what shape, was destined to be consumed by the work of war—like scraps of vegetables become soup.

One night, the lieutenant came to their squad tent

looking for volunteers to walk the railroad tracks to hunt Russian partisans, check for damage, and look for explosives.

Franz stood up and saluted the lieutenant. "You can count on us, sir," Franz said, speaking for the squad. Newly promoted to senior lance corporal, he was out to impress.

As soon as the lieutenant left, the squad members loudly complained to their overzealous friend. Martin Schimpf was among the most vocal. "Are you serious? Why take the risk?"

"Are you crazy?" Othman Faber, new to their squad, echoed Martin's concern.

"Why put us in the line of fire tonight?" Martin shouted.

Moore put his hands on his hips and challenged the group. "Are you chicken?" He turned to Stefan. "The Russians haven't yet made a bullet that can take us out, right, Stefan?"

Stefan shook his head. He had always admired Franz's spirit, but this *was* crazy. The Russian partisans were fighting for their land and homes. Their hearts were in the war. They were dangerous opponents.

Though Stefan believed that being in the infantry was more about guts and determination—the will to survive—than technical skill with a gun, there were limits. He had a family to think about, a family who needed him. But he did not want Franz to go without the protection of a friend.

The light of the moon illuminated the path to the railroad tracks.

"We're to walk the tracks and be on the lookout for torn-up rails and explosive charges. We will maintain silence. Speak only when absolutely necessary," Franz whispered.

The squad leader was at the point, followed by six riflemen, three on each side of the tracks. The MG 34 team of Schimpf, Faber, Stefan, and four other soldiers brought up the rear.

Rapid gunfire shattered the silence of the night.

In the opening rounds of the ambush, Martin crumpled. The trooper nearest the point man took one in the throat. At least eight shots fired from a submachine gun riddled Franz Moore, his body convulsing from the force of the bullets before he fell. Stefan dropped to the ground, but there was no cover in the snow. The other troopers scattered, a few wildly firing rifles on the run.

"Get back!" Stefan shouted.

His order to retreat was drowned out by the explosion of a partisan hand grenade landing in the brush several meters from the rail line. *The next will be more accurate,* he thought. German rifles laid down cover fire, allowing the five troopers in front of him to withdraw. As they passed, firing their weapons, Stefan followed, joining the cadre at the rear. Another grenade exploded, this one in the squad's line of fire but too far away to do damage.

Finding relative refuge in a crater by the tracks, Stefan sent three men to the right and three more to the left. "Go out wide and flank them," he directed. He spread the other remaining troopers out with orders to lay down as much continuous fire as possible. Crawling from one man to the next, he distributed ammunition and urged them on.

At the height of the battle, Stefan looked up to see more enemy coming from the woods. He instinctively reached for his Maschinenpistole before realizing he was unarmed. A shell-shocked soldier walked directly into the line of fire. Stefan screamed at him and attempted to pull him back, but he was too late. Bullets ripped through the man's body, and he crumpled. An alert soldier whirled around and laid down gunfire in the direction of enemy muzzle flashes. A second later, several grenade explosions quieted the snipers.

"Check them out," Stefan ordered. Two-man teams searched enemy bodies.

Stefan walked to the fallen German soldiers. He reached Martin Schimpf's body and knelt down beside him. Tears filled his eyes. Martin, a boyhood friend who had been at his wedding and had served with him in the Romanian army, was dead. He gently closed his eyes for the last time. He did not know Othman Faber or the other troopers well, but they too were dead. He collected their metal identity tags and placed them in his pocket.

Finally, Stefan walked slowly to the body of his friend, Franz Moore, dreading what he would see. He remembered the boy with the freckled face who loved to dance and was so eager to join the army. Together they had built the best wagon in town, rolled smokes from stolen tobacco, and shared a happy evening at the spinning where Stefan received Maria's first kiss. That was a lifetime ago.

Stefan went down on his knee by Franz's body. His heart was heavy. In the darkness, he whispered to his friend one last time. "Franz, you were right. They did not make one bullet for you. They made a lot of them." He removed Franz's metal identity disks and slipped them in his pocket along with the others.

Over the next few months, Stefan moved across countries, following his orders. While stationed in Parczew, Poland, he trucked food back and forth from the border to the war zone. Then transferred to Danzig, Poland, he trained recruits and took them back to Russia. In Russia, while moving ammunition, his unit captured several Russian soldiers. The Russians were wearing American underwear, socks, smoking American cigarettes, and chewing American gum. Even their boots were American. The sight caused a knot to form in Stefan's stomach. If Americans were supplying the Russians, he knew the war would end badly for Germany. It was only a matter of time.

In the litany of all of his worries, a new one emerged: with America fighting Germany, would he ever be welcome in America?

In December, he was no longer in Russia. Germany was no longer driving the front; instead, the front was coming to them. American and British air forces clouded the skies with their planes, following German tank tire tracks and peppering the snow with bombs. There was nowhere to go; Germany was losing ground.

It was Christmastime, and it was cold. Stefan had been away from his home and family for eight months in a war that made no sense. He had seen more death and destruction than he could have ever imagined. He was no longer naïve. He was tired and lonely. He wanted to see his family—to hold Maria again, to kiss his children, to sleep in his own bed.

Stefan returned to camp one night weary from another day of driving supplies. His commanding officer handed him an envelope with his name on it. He turned away to open it, feeling bitter, as he wondered about this new set of orders. Where would they send him next?

He opened the envelope and read it repeatedly. He could not believe it. He had been given a furlough. He was going home!

CHAPTER SIXTEEN

"There is not enough darkness
in all the world
to put out the light of even one small candle."
Robert Alden

Scheindorf to Slovakia
Winter 1943 to October 1944

GERTRUDE WALKED FROM the kitchen, her hand cupped around the flickering candle. She leaned down and placed it on its plate on the front windowsill. The welcome light burned every night in the hope that her son would return home. She looked out the window on the cold winter evening and saw candles in the windows of neighbors with sons and husbands gone to war. Though Christmas had passed, the glow from the candles made the winter evening seem a little brighter.

The sky was still light from the setting sun, and an approaching line of dark purple clouds promised more snow. Even as she watched, light snow, in big flakes, started to fall. She sighed, pulled her rosary from her pocket, and prayed as she looked out the window.

"Oma, I'm going to put the girls to bed now," Maria

called from the kitchen.

"I'll be right there," Gertrude said. "I'll say their prayers with them."

———•—•———

Stefan walked the last few kilometers in the freezing cold of the early evening. His energy—invigorated by the news that he was going home—had long ebbed. Since receiving his furlough just before Christmas, the journey from the front toward home had taken him six long weeks.

He had boarded trains that stopped and never continued. Found rides on trucks and then walked so far his feet blistered. He had slept in barns, in the forest under piles of leaves, and in railway stations. He was so tired, he felt as if he were walking in a dream. The stress of constantly being in the line of fire for so many months ate away at him, even now that he had left the war temporarily behind. Though he could not remember when he'd last had hot food or a warm place to sleep, the silence of his journey was soothing. There was no gunfire. There were no screams of dying men.

Will the girls remember me? He had not seen his family for nine months. Nine months was a long time in the life of a child.

He remembered that.

———•—•———

Gertrude prayed, looking out the window.

"St. Anthony, send him home," she whispered.

She saw a figure walking down the middle of the street. He carried a rucksack on his back. She shook her head. *Another stranger looking for food.* Every day, it seemed, men traveling through would knock on the door, begging for food. She fed them what they had, hoping that somewhere, a kind woman would feed her son. The night was falling. Was he looking for shelter too?

The man kept walking closer, looking at the house. She nearly put the candle out. She was tired, weary of war and worry. She did not want to feed another stranger tonight.

Then she looked again, peering close to the window, her breath fogging the glass.

She recognized the walk.

"*Stefan,*" she whispered to herself. "Stefan!" she shouted to the house. She opened the door and ran out.

⸻

Maria had just put the girls in bed when she heard Gertrude shout. Was Opa okay? Why was Oma shouting?

Concerned, she left the girls and walked quickly to the open door. Opa and Oma were outside, their arms around a man.

My Stefan!

Maria's eyes filled with tears, and she ran out of the house. What she saw broke her heart. Stefan was gaunt, leaner than she had ever seen him. His auburn beard, long and ragged, was streaked with grey.

He looked up from his parents and saw her. His eyes

were shining with love.

Then his knees buckled from exhaustion.

She wrapped her arms around him and held him up. "You are safe now," she said. "You are home." He felt so thin. She brushed her cheek against his—it was rough and cold. She could feel the weariness in his bones.

"You kept me alive," he said to her. "All I could think about was coming back to you."

"Thank you, God," Gertrude said. "Thank you!"

"Come inside. It's cold out here," Maria said. "We still have some soup on the stove. I'll warm it up." She took him by the arm and guided, almost lifted him into the house.

Stefan walked into the house and stopped.

Two little blonde girls stood barefoot in their white nightgowns. Klothilde held Siglinda by the hand. They stared at him wide-eyed.

"What are you doing out of bed?" Gertrude said.

"We heard you," Klothilde said. Then she walked closer, pulling Siglinda with her. "Papa?"

"Yes." Stefan went down on his knees and wrapped them in his arms. He started to cry.

"Papa." Klothilde pulled away from his embrace. She pinched her nose with her fingers. "Papa, you need a bath."

Everyone laughed.

"Yes, I do," he said, wiping tears of laughter from his eyes. "Can I eat first?"

Stefan's three-week furlough, packed with family,

food, and conversation, was passing quickly. Maria was as beautiful as ever, and his daughters had grown— Klothilde was nearly five, and Siglinda, a baby when he left, would be two in July. He could not get enough of them.

Stefan's father was still mayor. Life in Scheindorf continued in the cycle of a farming community, but the villagers no longer lived in the purity and safety of political isolation. War had touched and tainted everything. Husbands, fathers, and relatives had died. Food and supplies were rationed or unavailable. The blissful sleep of ignorance was replaced by nightmares of worry. There were more questions than answers. War was not black and white; it was gray.

One night, Stefan and his father stayed up late talking alone in the wine cave.

"Pop, remember when you told me that when the Americans entered the Great War, it was then you knew we'd lose the war?"

His father nodded.

"Well, Germany is going to lose this war. The American dollar has arrived."

Stefan went on to tell his father about the Russian soldiers they had captured and their American gear. "They were even wearing American made boots. Some of our men have been without boots for months, wrapping our feet in burlap."

He talked in detail about the German army losing ground.

"The scope of the fighting, and Germany's limited resources—along with the Americans, British, and Russians in the war—is going to kill Germany. Hitler is insane."

Stefan was shocked by his own words, spoken aloud in the darkness of the cellar.

His father looked down at his hands and spoke.

"I'm reminded of a conversation I had many years ago in America, at Rosalia and Adolf's home—you remember the Pfitzner's, Gertrude's sister?"

Stefan nodded. "I never met them, Pop, but I know of them."

"It had to be 1922. I was working, trying to save money to bring you and your mother to America. It was one of the most hopeful and lonely times of my life." He paused, and his eyes filled with tears. "We had a conversation at the dinner table. My brothers were there. Mind you, this was twenty years ago. It was quite spirited." He smiled for a moment. Then he looked into Stefan's eyes, and his smile was gone. "It was about Hitler. Was he a lunatic or was he a great leader? Or was he both? Germany was very vulnerable when he first began to attract followers. Many of us interpreted his vision as one that would lead us to recovery and restore our greatness."

"But at what cost, Pop? If you'd seen what I've seen, you would understand. I was hoping that in this war I could protect our country—the village. Instead, I'm hunting Russian peasants who are fighting for their land. Taking their livestock, burning their houses built with their own hands. I'm learning of Jews being deported and killed—thousands of them. I've seen my friends die in front of me."

His father looked at him, and tears were in his eyes. "I never wanted you to have to go to war. This is not what I wanted for my son, my wife, or my grandchildren. I never expected anything like this. We were blind."

"We were hopeful, Pop. Everyone needs hope." He

reached over to squeeze his father's hand. "But now it is time to face the truth. Not what Hitler says, but what we see—what we actually witness. We're outmanned and outgunned. The Allies' airplanes are everywhere. Believe me—I've seen them. They have the money, the resources. No matter what Hitler says, Germany can't win this war."

He stared in his father's eyes for a long time. His father nodded.

"Pop, a lot of people are very angry at Germany—not just at the army, but at the German people, all of us. There is no morality in this war. Civilians are targets. Women are being beaten, raped, and killed. Property has been taken; people have lost their businesses, land, and homes because of what Germany has done."

His father stood up, took a deep breath, and let it out in a long sigh. "So what you are saying is that our hope in a better Germany has made us blind to what is really happening. Hitler has put lies in a pretty box and tied it with our hope. We believe it to be the truth—what we hear from our leaders. They tell us what they want us to believe. It is only propaganda—not the truth."

His father's words struck a chord. He understood. His father looked down, then at Stefan. "It's time to stop hiding our heads in the sand. If I don't find the truth, then I become a part of Hitler's cause."

"Yes, Pop. That's what I'm saying."

Stefan's heart was racing. He did not want to speak his fear. Spoken, it made it real. He said it anyway. "Just because we're in a small village does not mean Scheindorf will be safe."

Stefan took a deep breath and continued. "Pop, you're very political. Stay alert. Watch the signs. I don't know what is going to happen. I don't know how long you will be safe here. The Russians are moving from village to village. They may make it here. They don't care about children or women—except to use them, and then kill them."

Stefan stood up to face his father. His heart was full of dread. He knew he might not live through the war. He had to make sure his family was safe.

He met his father's eyes and spoke, "Pop, I need you to take care of my family—no matter what happens."

Judge Revak reached over and took Stefan's hand in both of his. He patted his son's hand and spoke.

"I promise to take care of them. Try not to worry. You will be back with us—when it is all over. We will start again. I can see it. I believe it." His father's eyes filled with tears. "Maybe, this time, we will finally be able to go to America."

The words almost broke Stefan's heart. How long would that dream last?

"I don't know, Pop. The war has made us enemies of America. We declared war on them. How will they ever forgive us?"

Stefan's trip back to his company took a circuitous path: Vienna, then Danzig, then Warsaw, and finally back to Russia. It took another six weeks. When he finally reached his company, he learned it had been destroyed and rebuilt three times. Now they were getting ready to reorganize yet again. All of his friends from Scheindorf were dead or had disappeared except for

Stefan Müntz, who had been declared unfit for duty after being shot in the chest. The men he served with now were strangers. They were walking dead men. None of them had a clue about the scope or progress of the war.

The feeling of hope he'd had while with his family quickly faded when he was back in the line of fire, once again running ammunition to the troops. He felt helpless, unable to defend himself or anyone else. His unit would hold a position for three or four days, and the Russians would push them back. Finally, after about a month, the Russians pushed them back nearly to the border. He wondered how he was still alive when everyone around him was dying.

It was impossible to serve with hope in a hopeless cause.

Stefan was transferred back to Warsaw to train the latest groups of recruits—some as young as thirteen. Months later, in the fall of 1944, he was in Slovakia training new recruits.

On October 8, 1944, he huddled around the radio with a few trusted soldiers listening to the BBC's Feind-sender station, the banned German-language reports that emanated from the enemy radio station in London. In the smoke-filled room, he learned that Russian soldiers had pushed the Germany army back. The boundary of war was approaching Satu Mare and Scheindorf.

Stefan was terrified. He felt helpless. He did not know how to warn them.

He knew they would have to evacuate. Leaving Scheindorf was the only move that could keep them safe. He had to trust that his father would take care of them.

He had to pray they would get out before it was too late.

CHAPTER SEVENTEEN

"There is much to love,
and that love is what we are left with.
When the bombs stop dropping,
and the camps fall back to the earth and decay,
and we are done killing each other,
that is what we must hold.
We can never let the world take our memories of love away,
and if there are no memories,
we must invent love all over again."
Louise Murphy

Scheindorf, Hungary/Romania
October 9, 1944

BEFORE DAWN ON that fateful morning, while the village slept in the blissful peace of ignorance, Maria knew what was coming. She knew what they had to do. They must leave everything familiar. The German officer who had come in the night had warned them. At first light, the judge would call a town meeting to tell the village what they must do.

Her mind raced. They would have to evacuate Scheindorf, the old and the young, the livestock, the wagons; they must plan and prepare provisions and shelter for the journey and organize the precious few possessions they could take with them. They would have to pack and leave quickly in order to hide from the encroaching Russian soldiers.

She had heard from Stefan of their cruelty. They would not hesitate to beat, rape, or kill the most vulnerable. How could she protect her daughters, just six and three, and pack for life on the run? She was leaving the only life she had ever known.

Her worry deepened with her concern for Stefan. How could she tell him they were leaving—where they were going?

Underneath all of it was a deep sense of loss. The hollow feeling in her heart told her that this life was over. Nothing would ever be the same.

Fear nearly paralyzed her. Stefan had warned them this might happen. Yet it was hard to believe. A flood of emotions rushed through her heart and mind, and she was overcome by anxiety. She took a few deep breaths. Prayer was always the path to peace, to guidance. So while she lay awake, not wanting to disturb her daughters, she prayed for their safe journey. Then she made mental lists of what they would need to do and what they should take with them.

It was still dark when she got up. Later she would mourn. Tomorrow she would worry. Now there was no time to waste.

She went into the kitchen and found Oma and Opa already at the table.

"We might as well eat all we can today," Gertrude said as she set down a cup of hot coffee before Maria. "This is the last of the coffee, Maria. We don't have any more."

"I know, Oma, the store has been out for weeks now."

Gertrude nodded. "I'll put together some soup and pick the last of the squash, parsnips, and cabbage in the garden. See what else I can find that will last awhile."

Maria poured fresh warm milk from a blue pottery pitcher into her cup and stirred her coffee. The brief moment of their morning routine stilled her heart. She took a sip of the coffee, and the bitter, rich taste and warmth felt good. Gertrude laid a bowl of hot cereal in front of her.

"Eat, Maria. You'll need it today."

She was not hungry, but she nodded her head and took a bite. The savory grain with a splash of milk coated her churning stomach. She looked up at Gertrude and said, "Thank you. It tastes so good today."

Gertrude nodded and smiled, but Maria saw her sadness.

"I'll take care of the girls, all of Stefan's things. Do you need help with the root cellar?"

"If you take care of the girls, I'll sort through all of the food. I'll empty the smokehouse. The meat will keep for a while. Better we take it with us than leave it for the Russians."

Maria saw her eyes flash with anger.

Judge Revak did not say anything. His shoulders were stooped with worry as he stared at his empty cup. Gertrude gave him more hot coffee. Then she rested her hand on his shoulder, leaned down, and gave him a soft kiss on the check. He patted her hand but did not look up. He picked up his spoon and stirred butter into the cup, deep in thought.

"Opa, I'll pray you find the right words," Maria said.

He looked at her and thanked her with his eyes, wet with tears. She could see his heart was breaking.

———•—•———

When Maria went outside the house that morning, German soldiers were swarming everywhere—in the barn where they tended the wounded, in the streets, in the fields. As word spread, the village buzzed with activity. At the town meeting, the judge, along with the German infantry officer, Hauptmann Georg Müller, explained to the people assembled that Scheindorf and the neighboring village of Hamroth, where Uncle Johan lived, would have to evacuate. The villagers were in danger. Judge Revak faced questions, tears, and anger. Why was this happening? What would they do?

Maria was no longer in shock. She felt the cold shadow of danger. On his furlough, months ago, Stefan had foretold Germany's loss of the war. Throughout the year, the Russian, American, and British forces had advanced across Europe. Nearly every major city had been devastated by air attacks. Now it was not just the cities, but also the countryside that must run and hide from war. Since the war had taken the young men from the village, the women, children, and older men made all of the preparations to leave. While Maria packed food, clothes, blankets, her precious linens, and a doll for each of the girls, Judge Revak, Gábriel, and Gertrude made a cover for their wagon. It would shelter them from the weather. Since Opa Ditzig was away serving in the German army, Oma Ditzig helped Frau Leili, Maria's grandmother, pack a small wagon.

That night at midnight, St. Anne's was open for confession. Maria slipped out of the house while the girls and their grandparents slept. As she walked to the church, she stopped for a moment and looked up at the moon. Where was Stefan? Was he looking at the same moon? It made her feel a little closer to him.

When she entered the church, it was quiet and peaceful—this holy place, the place of her wedding. That seemed like a lifetime ago. Hundreds of candles flickered in the darkness, and comforted by the familiar scent of beeswax and incense, she sighed. It was so beautiful.

No longer in motion, she realized how tired she was. She walked to their usual pew and knelt.

Others entered behind her, visiting the church for the last time. Their sorrow was palpable. The villagers hugged one another and wept, saying good-bye, with no idea what would become of them.

Maria fingered her rosary and started to pray to God, the Blessed Mother, and St. Anthony. She had a litany of prayers: for her husband's protection, that he would get word of their departure, for her father that he would return home from war, and for their safe journey. She prayed for the strength to do what was necessary to protect her children. After a few minutes, she made the sign of the cross, got up, and left the church. She had one more visit to make.

It was dark, but the moon was still bright as Maria walked through the church graveyard. She passed the stones of generations of relatives. She finally stopped before a small headstone—the headstone of a child. She leaned down to touch it.

"Good-bye, little sister. Mathilda, pray for us," she whispered. She could not hold back any longer. Maria wept alone in the night.

———•—•———

On October 10, 1944, at four o'clock in the afternoon, it was gray and raining softly as the Revak wagon carrying Stefan, Gertrude, Maria, Klothilde, and Siglinda left Scheindorf. Judge Revak had hitched his two strongest horses to the wagon, and they had shared what livestock they could with others. Sadly, they had to leave the old cows behind.

The wagon train of refugees stretched as far as Maria could see ahead and behind them. There were at least fifty wagons loaded with people she had known and loved for a lifetime. She looked over her shoulder at the girls, sitting in the back of the covered wagon, playing with their dolls. They were innocent and unafraid. She smiled.

"They won't remember," said Judge Revak. "They're too young."

Maria nodded.

Then she stole one final look at Scheindorf as it passed by and wondered if this exodus would be two weeks long or forever. Her eyes were dry. It was now time to look ahead, be a good mother to her children, and help others along the way.

The German soldiers who had come to warn them walked or rode alongside the trail of wagons guiding them to Austria. Though the military presence was reassuring, it also made her wonder what danger might be around the next bend in the road. Would the soldiers be able to protect the vulnerable villagers? Only God knew.

During the day, they rationed their supplies and collected food from the fields to feed the families, soldiers, and horses. At night, they made camp, shared what they had with others, and slept in the cold near whatever shelter they could find, sometimes taking cover by the warmth of the horses. Maria was not sure where they were going or how she would get word to Stefan. Was he still at his last posting? Had he moved?

In the silence and cold of the night, her daughters huddled around her for warmth, as she lay awake and worried. All she could do was pray.

———•••———

Somewhere in Slovakia
Fall 1944

Stefan was out of his mind with fear.

Where were they? He knew the Russians were closing in on his village. He should be with them, protecting them. Yet here he was, doing futile work, teaching new soldiers how to fight. Odds were the soldiers would end their young lives in battle or starve in the cold, strangers in a foreign land. No matter what he taught them, he could not guarantee their future.

Exhausted from worry and lack of sleep, Stefan trudged back to the barracks one cold afternoon. It looked like snow. The sky, with dark, gray low clouds, looked ominous. It was too early for a blizzard. Just what he needed: to train the new recruits in another night drill where they froze to death before they were hit by a stray shot.

Did someone call his name? He looked around.

"Revak! Revak! Telegram!"

He was so preoccupied that he had not seen the elderly postal carrier.

He ran toward the carrier, who held up an envelope when he saw Stefan. He had not heard from Maria for weeks. He did not know where they were, if the Russians had come, if they had escaped.

"Thank you! Thank you!" he said to the man.

Stefan reached for the envelope and tore it open. He had to know.

The telegram said, "Tomorrow we cross the Tisza. Don't come."

He reread the telegram. What were they doing at the river? They had left Scheindorf. They were at least five hundred kilometers from the village. What had happened? Who was with them?

But one thought overwhelmed the others: *Thank God they are safe!*

Stefan heard nothing more for weeks. Consumed by worry, he prayed.

Then another telegram came.

"We are in Austria, near Linz. Don't come."

They were hundreds of kilometers further away! What was happening? Stefan had never felt so helpless in his life, yet he had hope as long as his family was on the move. Was it possible they could escape the worst of the war? But even if they did, the long winter was ahead of them. Would they survive? How would he find them?

Altmünster, Austria
December 1944

On a bitterly cold and snowy day, after seven weeks of travel, the Scheindorf refugees arrived in Altmünster, Austria. The villagers found shelter through the Red Cross in many different locations. Uncle Anton and Aunt Anna, along with cousins Margaret Maria and Philip, Uncle Johan, and others, found shelter in an abandoned schloss. Oma and Opa, Maria, and the girls found housing in a schoolhouse with other refugees. It was more a barn than a school. There was no running water, no place to cook food, and no heat. Their bed was a pile of straw, but they found comfort in feeling safe and being together. They had a roof over their head for the first time in months. The wind howled all around them at night.

The Red Cross gave the refugees a small amount of food and secondhand clothing. Maria was distraught when little Siglinda started to itch, and she found her covered in red welts from body lice. Siglinda cried from the constant itching and bled from the bites. Lice were everywhere—in the clothes, the straw beds, the meager linen they found. There was no soap to wash clothes. There was no way to escape the lice that feasted on human blood while the refugees starved.

Maria prayed every day for Stefan's safety. She dreaded a visit from a telegraph boy, the "Angel of Death" as he was called, who would bring the notice of Stefan's death. She had sent two telegrams at post offices along the way. She had no way of knowing if he had received them. Did he know they had left Scheindorf? It had been months since she had heard from him. Though she worried terribly, she felt a strong and deep connection with her husband. She believed he was alive.

It had been six weeks since Maria sent the last telegram to Stefan. They had stopped moving from place to place. They would be in Altmünster for a while. She was desperate to see him. It was time to tell him to ask for a furlough and come.

———·•·———

Stefan trudged through the snow toward a low building, more a shed than a school. This was it—the address his wife had sent him, their new "home"? It had been weeks since he received Maria's telegram and got a furlough. The journey was long, by train, truck, and on foot. He was tired and cold, his stomach hollow with hunger. But all that mattered little. He smiled, and his heart beat rapidly with anticipation. He felt a rush of energy as he thought about seeing his family—holding them, kissing them. It had been so long. His exhaustion and hunger faded.

It was snowing heavily, huge fluffy flakes, and the snow was piling up in drifts around the door. He pulled with all of his strength to open it.

Stefan walked into the enclosure and fastened the door closed behind him. He turned around. Some thirty people were scattered around the room. Straw piles were their beds, wooden crates their tables and chairs. The room was freezing. Mothers sat breastfeeding their babies. Children, wearing all of their clothes to stay warm, played.

One by one, the pale faces in the room turned to

look at him.

He took off his hat and shook the snow from it.

"Stefan? Stefan, is that you?" Maria cried out.

His eyes filled with tears as he searched for her voice. From the shadows in the back of the room, she stood and walked quickly to him.

"You found us!"

They ran into each other's arms and cried.

Stefan held his wife close. He desperately kissed her forehead, her cheeks, and her lips. He would never let her go. *My treasure, my Schatzie.* She felt so thin. He pulled away from their embrace and looked at her. His beautiful wife was pale and gaunt, her once lustrous and curly hair pulled back from her face in a tight knot. Her clothes were threadbare and smudged with dirt.

What have we done? What has this war done to those we love? Our homes?

Despite his troubled thoughts, the sight of his wife brought him new life. It had been months since he had felt the solace of family. Even here, in this awful place, it was sweet.

Klothilde joined her mother, hugging her skirts.

"Papa?" she asked, looking up at Stefan like a stranger.

He picked her up and hugged her close. She threw her arms around his neck and held on tight—as if she would never let him go. Stefan smiled into the happy face of his oldest.

Siglinda stood by at a distance, holding her doll tightly to her chest.

"Siglinda," Maria said. "Come here. Say hello to your papa."

Siglinda hid behind her mother. Stefan's heart fell.

"She'll come around," Maria said. "She just does not

remember you—give her time."

A moment later, Stefan's father crushed him in a hug. The judge started to cry. Then the circle of the family grew when Gertrude joined them. Gratitude overwhelmed Stefan's heart. They were together, all safe.

"I knew you would find us," his mother said to him.

"Nothing would keep me away, Mama."

He could not stop hugging and kissing them. He was relieved to see them, yet devastated to discover their living conditions. What could he do to help them?

The answer was clear, but he did not want to accept it.

Nothing. There was nothing he could do but love them.

———

Stefan spent nearly two weeks in Altmünster. He found such peace being with family. He was happy to see his Uncle Anton and others. Yet he was deeply saddened to learn that his Aunt Anna had died in childbirth. Maria and Gertrude created communal meals of the meager food they could find. It was amazing what kind of soups could be made from scraps of meat and bits of vegetables. Siglinda finally warmed to him. He met the family who lived next to the school, the Hessenbergers, who had shared some clothes with his family. He had a few private talks with his father, sharing news about the war, not willing to frighten the others.

The time went quickly, and Stefan needed to return to his company. While on a train bound for Vienna, he stood with others in an overcrowded car, watching the snowy countryside pass by and wondering when he would see his family again. They were suffering. He felt helpless and guilty.

Suddenly, he felt an intense, sharp spasm in his back. His knees buckled. He held on to a seat to stand up, but dizziness and nausea pushed him to his knees again. His back had been a problem every now and then, but never this bad. He could hardly walk.

When the train reached Vienna, he got off, and a fellow soldier called Stefan's regimental headquarters. They ordered him to go to a hospital in Vienna. He was taken by ambulance to the hospital, where he was diagnosed with a slipped disc. He asked if his wife could come and take care of him. They sent a telegram, and Maria took the train to Vienna.

One night, while Stefan and Maria were in the hospital ward lined with beds filled with twenty other soldiers and civilians, they heard the wail of an air-raid siren. Then he heard the drone of multiple aircraft overhead. They were close.

A nurse in white entered the ward. "Come quickly," she commanded, her voice firm. "We must get you all to shelter in the basement. We are being bombed again."

Stefan saw fear on the faces of the patients and family members.

"Help each other," the nurse said. "Those of you who can walk, help others. I'll move beds to safety."

Maria helped Stefan out of bed. Then she walked over to another bed where a man lay with a bandage around his head. It covered his eyes. He was alone.

"Can you walk?" she said.

"Yes, but I can't see," he replied. "I was hit by glass during an air raid. I was running to a shelter."

"I'll be your eyes," she said.

Maria and Stefan got on either side of the man and started to move toward the stairs that would take them down to the shelter.

A high-pitched whistling sound filled the air, and then another as the bombs fell. The dark room lit up like a flash of daylight, and a boom shook the building. The windows shattered, and a gust of hot hair blew splinters of glass like daggers across the room. Chunks of plaster fell from the ceiling.

Stefan wrapped his arms around both of their shoulders and crouched lower, pulling them both down with him. "Move! Move!" he shouted.

They headed down the hall to the stairs as fast as they could, stepping over chunks of debris, holding the blind man on either side, guiding him so he would not fall.

"Vienna has been bombed dozens of time," the man said. "We're sitting ducks in this hospital. The Americans bomb us like clockwork, same time of day. We call them waves of death."

Stefan and Maria looked at each other, thinking the same thought. They had children who needed them.

They continued their conversation with the man as they walked down the stairwell toward the shelter. The bombing had stopped for a few minutes.

"Are you from Vienna?" Maria asked.

"Yes," he replied. "I may never see again, but I'll remember beautiful Vienna with our parks and gardens, the opera house, the palaces. In 1939 when Hitler wanted Austria, he called Vienna 'a pearl to which he would give a proper setting.' To see the city now, and I am glad I cannot, it is a pile of rubble. Our history, our buildings and art, are gone. Most of Vienna lives in air-raid shelters. Our Jewish friends have disappeared. Independent from Germany we would have been safe, but they made us a part of their war. This is what Germany has done to us."

Stefan flinched, once again feeling the devastating impact of war. He wondered what the man would feel if he realized that Stefan was a German soldier.

They made it safely to the basement and huddled there with other patients and family members. The bombing lasted through the night. The building shook with the blasts.

The bombing finally stopped, and the silence a balm to their senses. Stefan brushed the bits of plaster and dust from Maria's hair. She smiled at him and shook her head. "My ears are still ringing," she said. "I don't know how families can live like this."

A man in a white coat came into the shelter. He looked around, nodding, taking stock of the situation.

"Could I have your attention please?" he said. The room quieted. "My name is Dr. Heinrich Bauer. I am the hospital medical director. It is not safe here. We've been badly damaged. If you live in Vienna, you need to find shelter with family and friends. We will help you. If you are a soldier and live within fifty kilometers of the hospital, we will give you a pass. You can go home and recover. If you need medication, if we have it, we will provide it for you."

Stefan looked at Maria. She took his hand.

"We live about seventy kilometers away," Stefan said. "Can you help us? I need a pass."

"Let me see what I can do," Dr. Bauer said.

After a few hours, Stefan received a pass. They said good-bye to the blinded man, who thanked them for their aid. They returned to Altmünster, where Stefan took his medication, rested, and spent Christmas with his family. Then it was back to war.

PART IV

CHAPTER EIGHTEEN

"Every person in Germany should realize that this time Germany is a defeated nation . . . The fact that they are a defeated nation, collectively and individually, must be so impressed upon them that they will hesitate to start any new war."
Franklin D. Roosevelt

Russian occupied Germany to Silesia to Saxony, Germany
1945

NINETEEN FORTY-FOUR was a devastating year for Germany. By the end of the year, Romania, Bulgaria, and Hungary had joined the Allies. The Allies had retaken nearly every square mile of German-conquered territory. Russia was free. The Allied air and shell attacks not only targeted German bridges and railroads but also demolished cities and villages. Millions of German soldiers and civilians were dead. Panicked refugees clogged roads and rail stations, preventing the German army from staging a fighting retreat against the Russians.

When a *Feldpost* from Maria caught up with Stefan, he learned that his family, including his father and mother, were now living in a two-room apartment in Altmünster. Maria was cleaning houses, and his father had started a delivery service using the wagon they drove from Scheindorf. *Thank you, God!* It was a rare piece of good news, and Stefan tucked the note into his field jacket close to his heart.

As the Red Army kept moving toward him, Stefan kept moving back. Reassigned from one unit to another, he did whatever was needed—carrying their meager supplies, ammo, and food. The only thing he could not do was fire an automatic weapon. Though he managed to shoot his Lugar pistol, his aim was poor.

Since regular supplies were no longer reaching his unit, they rationed food and were careful with their supply of ammunition. Men had gone without new boots for months. The winter had cost many soldiers their fingers and toes, lost to frostbite and gangrene. Boots, scavenged from dead soldiers they found frozen in the fields, were their salvation.

Driven deeper into Russian occupied Germany that April, they had one hope: to make it to American occupied territory. There they would surrender. They knew they had no hope of winning the war. They would take their chances with the Americans.

One evening, at dusk, Stefan's unit emerged from the forest into a cornfield. He could see a farmhouse and barn in the distance. They had lost their bearings, but the Captain thought they might be near the near the border of Germany and Czechoslovakia.

"If it's empty, let's camp there," Captain Weber said pointing to the house.

"Sounds good to me," Stefan said as we walked with the captain. "If we're lucky, they might have some food in the root cellar."

"Better yet, a cow in the barn," said Corporal Schmidt.

"Or a pig in the yard," said Corporal Schneider.

"Fan out and scout the area," Weber said. "Make sure there aren't Russians on our heels. Revak, take Schmidt and Schneider with you. The rest of you, start gathering wood."

As the Stefan led the small team of men along the perimeter of the forest, listening and watching for the enemy, they heard movement in the woods. Stefan held up his hand to signal quiet. They held their position, guns ready. The sound of branches breaking and footsteps on the crusty snow got closer.

Suddenly, they saw a young woman come toward them. She did not see them. She was weaving her way through the trees, picking up kindling, and putting the sticks in a large basket. She looked like a young Maria, very pretty with dark curly hair that cascaded from under a red wool hat.

They stood still as she approached. She saw them. Her eyes went wide with surprise and fear. She turned around and started to run through the woods, but Schneider chased after her, grabbing her by the arm, forcing her to return to the small circle of soldiers.

"She could give away our position," Schneider said in German. "We must kill her."

"No, no—she's just a young girl. Why would she warn the Russians? After what they do to women," Stefan said.

"We'll have to let the Captain decide," Schneider glared at Stefan. "I'm not going to let one girl get me killed after getting this far."

Stefan followed Schmidt and Schneider who dragged

the girl between them. She fought, kicking and biting them. Schmidt stopped and hit her across the face. Stefan saw her anger flash, and she reached up to wipe her bloody mouth with her hand.

When the soldiers and their prisoner came to Captain Weber, they told him the story. He nodded.

"Revak," he said. "You can shoot that Lugar, right?"

"Yes, sir," Stefan said.

"Take her into the woods and shoot her," Weber said. "If the Russians find her, they will do something worse."

Stefan's conscience struggled with his passion to stay alive.

The young woman watched the interchange, looking from one man to the next. She looked angry and confused. Her dark eyebrows furrowed. She did not speak.

Stefan's heart fell. They were now killing defenseless, innocent women. He walked up to her, reached for her arm, and led her into the forest. He looked back at his company who followed him with their eyes and nodded. They wanted her dead. She was a small price to pay for their safety.

Stefan guided her through the forest. She did not resist. His hand was firm on her arm and he had not drawn his weapon. When they were nearly a half kilometer away, they came to a clearing. He stopped and dropped her arm.

"Back away," he said.

She shook her head. Her eyes, shining with tears, pleaded with him for mercy.

"Move away," he motioned with his hand.

She took a few steps back, her eyes never leaving his.

He took out his Lugar. She froze in fear. Her lips trembled.

He aimed and fired three times.

Shock and surprise widened her lovely green eyes. Hugging her arms across her chest, she looked down in disbelief at the ground where he had shot.

"Now run!" Stefan said to her. "Get out of here!"

She needed no more encouragement, and she raced through the trees away from Stefan.

He holstered his Lugar and headed back to his unit.

———————

That night, Stefan's unit slept deeply. Their stomachs were full of the chickens they slaughtered and roasted over the fire. The potatoes they pulled from the ground were still good, and nestled in the coals of the fire, they warmed their hands and put an end to their hunger. They sheltered in the empty farmhouse. They had even found some apple wine hidden away under the stairs. They felt safe. The girl, the witness to their presence, was dead.

Before dawn, Stefan woke. He heard the sound of a creaking door. Someone must have left to go to the out-house. He dozed off.

Suddenly, he heard boots stomp up the stairs and shouts from the first floor.

"Get out! Get out!" in Russian. Stefan sat up in bed just in time to see a Russian soldier barge into the room. The Russian thrust the muzzle of his gun into Stefan's forehead. His face was grim. Stefan raised his arms. The Russian backed away and motioned with his gun for

Stefan to move.

Stefan and his company were marched out of the farmhouse. They were in various stages of dress; some had slept in their clothes, others in their underwear. It was cold. One of the Russian soldiers came out carrying all of the German weapons. He threw them on the ground.

"We surrender," said Captain Weber.

"It's too late for that," said the Russian officer in German. His stern voice was impatient and seethed with loathing.

Russian soldiers gave Stefan's unit field shovels.

"Dig your graves—there," he pointed. "One big hole should do it. Now get to work. I promise your deaths," he snapped his fingers "will be quick."

Stefan could not believe what he was hearing. Had the young woman given them away? Or what this just bad luck?

The Russian soldiers shoved the Germans forward to the flat area where they were to dig their graves. Stefan felt overwhelmed by waves of sadness. He had come this far, to die and be buried in an unmarked grave. Maria would never know what happened to him.

He looked at the Russian solder nearest him. The soldier looked at him with eyes full of regret. Was he thinking that this could be his fate someday? Stefan wondered.

Stefan desperately needed to relieve himself. Seeing the glimpse of empathy in his captor's eyes, he thought he might be allowed to make one last visit to the outhouse. He got the soldier's attention and motioned to the outhouse. The soldier nodded. Stefan walked toward the outhouse, looking back to see if he would be shot, but the soldier was following him, his gun pointed at Stefan's back.

Stefan went into the outhouse. He could smell smoke from a cigarette as the guard waited outside. He leaned against the wall. The board was loose. *Was it loose enough to get out?* He did not stop to think of the consequences if caught. He pushed. The board gave way with a small squeak. Stefan shouldered his way through and ran into the woods. He never looked back.

———◦•◦———

A few days later, Stefan caught up with another German unit who was also trying to evade the Russians. They were in the region of Silesia, near Czechoslovakia. One morning, he was awakened by a German officer shouting, "Everybody up! Everybody up! No shooting!" All around, there was mass confusion. No one knew what was going on. He got up, collected his gear, and walked with his unit to a large pasture. There were thousands of German soldiers and civilians milling around.

Why is everyone here? Many of the soldiers were upset, looking angry or sad. People were crying. Other soldiers were happy, slapping each other on the back, laughing. Civilians looked the same way—some happy and some sad. Why such mixed emotions?

Stefan approached an older man, who stood apart on the edge of the crowd, watching and smoking a cigarette.

"What is going on?" Stefan asked. "Do you know? Why are all of these people here?"

The man was tall and lean, his clothes patched and

ragged. He looked at Stefan with wise blue eyes.

"Are you career military?"

"No," Stefan said vehemently. "I'm a farmer, a father and husband. I'm only in the army because I was called to serve."

"Then you will be happy," the older man said. He took another drag of his cigarette.

Stefan was even more puzzled.

The man looked him in the eyes and said, "Son, the war is over. Germany has surrendered."

It took a moment for the impact to hit, and then joy flooded Stefan's heart and mind. He could be with his family! *Thank you, God!*

"What about Hitler? I thought he would never give up," Stefan said.

"Hitler is dead. He committed suicide on April 30. Germany surrendered on May 7."

The words hung in the air, and Stefan felt a deep sense of relief. The driving force behind the war was dead. Everyone could go home, find their families. Return to life without war. But what was left? How many thousands would have to rebuild or start all over? It could never be the same. Mothers and wives had lost sons and husbands; children had lost fathers. Death was forever. Bricks and mortar could rebuild a house, but never seeing the face of a husband again or feeling the warmth of his embrace, never sharing a simple meal, going to bed every night alone—these things would leave a desolation that would last until the end of life.

Anger flashed forward and quickly pushed his feelings of relief aside. The monster Germany had believed in, trusted, and obediently followed into war had escaped. He had chosen his own way to die. Hitler had lied, killed innocent people because of their heritage, and put the youth of the country in the path of war. His greed and his quest for power had made Germany the enemy of the world. Hitler would never face the consequences of the devastation he had created, while everyone else would. He was a spineless coward.

Stefan's anger was galvanizing. It was time to move forward, find Maria, and create their future—whatever that might be. Later, he would deal with the painful memories of what he had endured. He had lost his dear friends, his home, years with his wife and children, his livelihood. The list of losses went on and on. There would be time for sorting through that later. Thanks to the grace of God, he was alive, and the most precious things in life were still waiting for him: his wife and family. He had not lost them.

The older man looked into his eyes, reading his thoughts.

"The things you feel now," the man said. "Look around you. These people feel many emotions—just like you. Career military men are angry and disappointed. Wives are hoping for their husbands' return. Soldiers have lost their cause. Germany is defeated. The German people have been fed lies for a long time. Where are we now? I don't know." Looking around, the man said, "It is not over. This is just the beginning."

The man turned around and walked away. Stefan watched him go, weaving his way through the crowd. He watched him until he disappeared into the mass of people.

A man called for attention over a megaphone. Stefan moved closer to the sound.

"Attention! Attention! The war is over. Everyone

go home. No more shooting. The war is over. Go home."
The man walked through the throngs of people repeating
the message.

The crowd started to move. Stefan followed. He saw
a wagon near the edge of the meadow. People were
storming it, helping themselves to food and clothing.
He joined them and was able to find a new black uniform,
cigarettes and cigars, and some salami. He quickly
changed out of his old clothes and felt almost human
again. Meat had never tasted so good. Now he would
find Maria. He was not sure how, but he would find her.

Thousands of soldiers and civilians with children
moved toward the roads, congested with hundreds of
trucks and military vehicles overloaded with people.
Traffic crawled in both directions. A truck slowed down,
and Stefan jumped on.

"Where are we going?" he asked.

"Toward the Tatra Mountains," said an officer in an
SS uniform.

Stefan hung on. The truck was bursting with people,
crying babies, men in tattered clothing. He was exhausted
but hopeful. He knew of the Tatras, the highest mountains
in the Carpathian Mountain range in northern Czechoslovakia. He would have to cross them to get to his
family. This was good.

Stefan looked back at the line of trucks making their
way to the mountains. Several of the men near him
were talking.

"There is still fighting going on," one man said.

"The Red Army occupies most of this area. They are
butchers," said the SS officer. "Germany has occupied
this area for years. We should fight. It's our duty."

Stefan kept his thoughts to himself. He was finished

with war. He had seen too much devastation, too many atrocities. The memories gave him nightmares—when he could sleep at all. What he knew made him worry even more about his family. They were still vulnerable. All he could think about was surviving. He kept his family alive in his heart. He would find them. He did not know how. *Protect me*, he prayed to God. *Protect my family.*

In the early evening, the truck started driving up into the hills of the Tatra Mountains. It would be a long journey, over five hundred kilometers.

They drove for hours into the night. Stefan dozed. He was jostled awake when the truck came to a stop.

"What's going on?" he asked.

They had come to a roadblock. He heard the conversation between the truck driver and some German soldiers.

"Everybody out!"

Armed German soldiers surrounded the truck, repeating, "Everybody out!"

The tank truck of people spilled out into the cold night air. Stefan was freezing. "What's going on?" he asked one of the soldiers.

"Russians are in the hills. It is too dangerous. You have women and children."

"Women and children can face this cold?" Stefan said.

"Better take their chances in the woods, on foot, then in this noisy truck," the soldier replied. "Everybody out!"

People ringed the truck, clutching their belongings or their children, uncertain what to do.

"Back away!" a soldier ordered. "Back away! If we

can't use this truck, no one will."

The soldiers planted charges around the truck and detonated them. A loud explosion shattered the silence of the night. Twisted pieces of metal and glass flew into the air, and the black night blazed bright from the fire that shot up into the sky.

Stefan, with the Maschinenpistole strapped to his back and the Lugar hidden in his rucksack, began the trek into the hills with five other men. They were a motley group—some emaciated from starvation, others heavy and out of shape. They stayed away from the road. The climb was tough. Though Stefan was cold, the exertion kept him warm.

"Best to keep quiet," said Leo, a German soldier from Yugoslavia.

"We have to worry—not only about the Russians but Czech partisans," another man said as he struggled to catch his breath.

"I need to rest," said another man, likewise breathing hard. "Go ahead, I'll catch up."

"We are not safe," Leo worried aloud. "The Czechs hate us. The Russians hate us. The Americans hate us."

Stefan kept silent, concentrating on his footing, putting all of his energy into breathing and the climb.

All night they climbed. They slept during the day, covering themselves with dry leaves to keep warm. When they reached the plateau at the summit, Stefan and Leo were the only ones left. Stefan could only hope the others would make it.

A town was visible in the distance, beyond a river. Leo pointed, "Look—the Elbe River. It borders Czechoslovakia through Germany. Yes?"

"Yes, it must be," Stefan said. "Let's rest for a while.

It's daylight. Time to take cover. We can start again in a few hours."

"Maybe we can find something to eat down there, yes?"

Stefan shook his head. "I'm hungry too, but I'll take safety over food. Let's rest, then walk down there and see what we can find—without being caught."

After they rested, Stefan and Leo walked down the steep incline through the woods, slipping and sliding through the leaves and mud. They could see the Elbe River clearly. Several boats were moored along the banks. A path wound its way along the riverbank, and two men and two women were walking it.

They ducked and hid in a ditch.

"We need to steal a boat and cross the river," Stefan whispered.

"What if they've seen us?" Leo asked. "We should kill them. They could tell others."

"No, no," Stefan said, shaking his head. "The men were looking at the pretty girls. They did not see us. Let's wait until we're sure they've gone."

About fifteen minutes later, they were ready to make a run for a boat. Suddenly, a dozen Czechs surrounded them.

"Hands in the air! Drop it!" The man motioned with his gun to Stefan's gun.

Stefan dropped his machine gun, gripped by fear. This could not happen—not now, not when they were so close! One of the men picked up the gun and smashed it against a tree, breaking it into bits.

"Move it!"

With guns roughly shoved in their backs, Stefan and Leo, their hands held high over their heads, were herded to the town square. The Czechs surrounded them and began to beat them, punching and kicking, crushing bones with the butts of their guns. They fell to the ground. Outnumbered, they did not resist. After what seemed like hours, the Czechs finally tired of the beating and left them in the middle of the square.

Lying on the cobblestones, racked with pain, Stefan thought he was going to die. But the very thought spurred him on. The war was over. There was no way he was going to die in this village! The knife-like pain in his ribs made every breath an agony, and his head throbbed. The lights of the town began to blur and then dim.

The next morning, a man prodded him with a rifle, waking him. The man motioned with his rifle for them to move and then waved his hand, directing them to get up and leave.

Stefan's eyes were swollen shut. He could barely see. His ribs had to be broken; they screamed with pain. But he got up and moved. They had to get out of the village. Stefan limped with Leo to a road where they joined a steady stream of civilians and soldiers.

After a few hours, two young men came up to Stefan. At gunpoint, they demanded his uniform and watch. They did not care about Leo—his clothes were torn and ragged. Leo kept walking. Stefan undressed, and the men took his clothes. He stood in the middle of the road in his underwear, in the cold. Aching and discouraged, he kept walking.

I have been through worse, Stefan told himself. *I am not dodging bullets. The war is over. I'm on my way to my family.*

After a few minutes, a woman came up to him.

"You look so sad—you must be cold," she said. "When

we get to the trees ahead, follow me. I have something for you."

He was not sure what to expect, but he could hear and feel her compassion, so he followed her into the woods. The woman opened her suitcase and pulled out a blue uniform—a shirt and pants. He was overwhelmed by her kindness. The pants were too small, but they offered more protection than underwear. Grateful and a little bit warmer, he walked down the road with the woman, carrying her suitcase.

After a few miles, once again, men robbed Stefan of his clothes. He could not believe it, but he kept moving. Another woman came to his aid, supplying him once again with new clothes. He was cold and sore. He had no money, no food. He kept walking along with everyone else.

Hours of walking passed, and up ahead, they saw soldiers on the road. They appeared to be searching everyone. Stefan still had the pistol in his bag, so he fished it out and dropped the gun in a clump of bushes on the side of the road. He did not want to be caught carrying a gun.

At the checkpoint, a soldier patted his bag down for weapons. Feeling nothing, he opened the bag, saw Stefan's cigarettes, and reached in to take them. After all he had endured, Stefan's pent-up anger boiled over. Enough of no rules! Of no respect for others!

"You have no right!" Stefan pulled the bag away from the thief. "I have no weapon. You have no right to take my personal things."

The soldier stared at him a moment and then snapped, "Come with me."

Stefan could not believe what was happening. It was

a simple thing. He just wanted his cigarettes. After everything he had lost, he was now being taken from the line for protecting one of his last meager possessions.

They marched Stefan to a house where a number of men were sitting around talking and smoking.

"What did they find on you?" one of the men asked.

Stefan was annoyed. He said, "Nothing. They found nothing on me."

"You wouldn't be here if they found nothing," the man said. He put out his cigarette and stood up. He gave Stefan a long look, taking in his bruises and his mismatched clothing, and shook his head in disgust.

Stefan held out his hands. "I have no guns or weapons. I just have some cigarettes, and I pulled my bag away at the checkpoint because I wanted to keep them."

"Are you sure?" said a young woman. She was making a list of names and items.

"I'm positive."

"Wait here. We need to verify that what you say is true."

One of the men left to find out who had searched Stefan. After a few minutes, he returned.

"I couldn't find him. Wait here."

Stefan waited still cold and growing more uncomfortable by the moment. A growing pressure in his bladder made standing still hard. He cleared his throat.

"What is it?" one of the men asked.

"I need to relieve myself," he said.

The man nodded toward an outhouse on the edge of the property. "Go," he said.

Stefan limped across the yard and let himself into the outhouse. He relieved himself. As he was about to leave he wondered, could he escape again? He noticed a shaft of light coming through the side. A board was loose.

Seizing the opportunity, he pushed the board out. He could escape. It seemed that every way he turned, some obstacle stood in his way. Well, he would go around this one. Taking a deep breath, he squeezed out the back of the outhouse and ran a zigzag path up into the hills, ducking behind bushes and trees to stay out of sight.

He heard gunfire behind him. Unsure if they were shooting at him, he kept running. He could do this. He made it to the forest and hiked up into the hills. Hours later, he rejoined the crowd of refugees.

The mass of humanity finally came to a fork in the road. Word passed down the line: "The road to the right goes to Saxony; the Americans are there. If you go to the left, the Russians are there." Stefan decided to take his chances with the Americans. *They always have food,* he thought. He wanted nothing to do with the Russians.

The group divided, some going to the right, some to the left. Stefan's group headed up into the mountains again. He was about five hundred yards up the hill in a moving throng of thousands of people. Looking down, he could see the Russians below. The road was jammed with refugees.

Suddenly they heard screams. All eyes followed the sound, which came from the crowd of people on the road below. Two Russian soldiers were dragging a woman from the line. She fought them, kicking and pulling away. Another woman tried to help her escape, and a soldier brutally nailed her with the stock of his rifle. She fell to the ground and did not get up. The soldiers picked up the young woman and carried her into the bushes.

No one else tried to help her. Stefan felt powerless to act. If he did, he would be shot. He was not a coward, but he was not a fool.

The woman's screams had alerted a Russian officer, who rushed to the scene a few minutes later. He took out his pistol, leveled it at the soldiers, and yelled, "The war is over! The war is over! This stops now! Everything like this stops! Everyone is going home!" Then he shot the soldiers who had raped the woman. They crumpled to the ground, dead.

Walking in the crowd, it took Stefan about a week to get to Saxony, Germany, where there were villages. There was no food or shelter along the way. He slept under blankets of leaves, drank from streams, and ate what few berries he could find in the woods.

When he reached Saxony, he knew he could no further without some kind of sustenance. Exhausted and hungry, in pain from his injuries, he wandered around searching for work. He knew there had to be work. Most of the able-bodied men in the area were away in the army. Stefan guessed that many would never come home.

He finally found a man working on a flagstone roof. He called up to the man. "Hello! Can you help me?"

The man climbed down the ladder. He wore a frayed and faded white straw hat. His piercing blue eyes, crinkled with wrinkles, were set deep under bushy gray eyebrows. His face was pink from the warmth of the day. A thick silver beard, neatly trimmed, surrounded his face like a smile.

"Johann Gloss." The man reached out to shake Stefan's hand.

"Stefan Revak—I'm looking for work. I had to leave my family, our farm, to serve in the German army. My family lived in Scheindorf, Romania, now Hungary, but they had to leave because of the war. I don't know if Scheindorf is even there anymore."

Johann nodded, listening.

"I have nothing now but my family—no clothes, food, or money. I will work for food, a little money, and a place to sleep. When I have saved enough money and regained my strength, I will travel to Austria, where they were last, and find my wife and two daughters."

Johann nodded again. "My son-in-law is in the German army. We have not heard from him for some time. Isabelle lives with us. She worries all the time." He looked down for a moment and then met Stefan's eyes. "As I'm sure your wife does." He paused. "How old are your daughters?"

"Let me think. Klothilde is seven and Siglinda four."

"They need their father," Johann said. "I always need an extra hand. We'll find you a place to sleep. We'll pay you as we go, all right?"

Stefan was so relieved and touched by the man's kindness that his eyes filled with tears. "Thank you," he said, reaching out to shake Johann's hand. "Thank you. You have saved my life."

"We need to find you some clothes. And you should wash up a bit before you meet the ladies of the house," Johann laughed.

Stefan laughed with him. He must be a sight, threadbare clothes, unshaven and dirty. It didn't matter. Everything would be all right now.

A few days later, American soldiers arrived in the area, registered everyone in the villages, and brought in provisions: food, blankets, clothing and shoes, winter coats, even sheets for the beds. They placed all of the supplies in a room at the school and put Stefan in charge of handing out them out. He brought home some food and blankets to the Gloss family.

Since they did not have a radio, after dinner at night Johann and his wife, Henrike, and their daughter, Isabelle, would sit around and talk with Stefan. Isabelle had learned from gypsies how to read fortunes. Stefan told her the story of meeting Cappi and his mother's concern about anyone ever knowing about their riding with the Roma. It seemed like it had happened in another life. It was so long ago, but it felt good to remember. It brought a smile to his heart. *Where is Cappi?* he wondered, then worried. Had Cappi been caught in the net and sent to a work camp? *Is he still alive?*

One evening, by the warm light of candles, Isabelle dealt the cards and told Stefan his fortune. She already knew about his family, that they had left their home and were refugees.

Her dark brows furrowed as she looked down at the cards. "I see that there is a lot of trouble ahead of you. But everything will be okay." She looked up and smiled at Stefan. "You will be lucky and go home quicker than you think."

Her sky-blue eyes met his. He was not sure what to believe, but it was interesting.

She continued, "You will cross a big body of water. There you will be very successful in business." She shook her head sternly and said, "But never have a partner— partnership does not look good for you."

He smiled and thanked her, wondering what it all meant. He had already gone through a lot of trouble. There was more to come?

———•—•———

Stefan had been with the family for about two weeks when one night after dinner, he and Johann were sitting side by side on the porch, enjoying the summer breeze. He was beginning to regain some of his strength. His bruises had healed. His ribs were mending. He felt safe. He had fallen into the rhythm of the family's life. Soon he would be able to travel—to find his family. God had put the Gloss family in his path.

The sun was setting; ribbons of pink and gold streaked across the sky. It was the end of another warm day. Stefan could smell freshly cut grass—such a comfort after so many years of gunpowder, smoke, and death. The smell of the earth, so rich with promise, made him ache with longing for home.

"It's been a rough few years for Germany," Stefan said.

Johann nodded, his teeth clenched around an empty wooden pipe. His chair creaked as he rocked back and forth. The sound was soothing.

"Can I tell you something?" Stefan asked abruptly.

Johann looked over at him. "Of course. You haven't said much of anything since you arrived—a few stories. I liked the one about the gypsies." The older man smiled. "I know you had a home and family, a father and mother. I know you were a German soldier. That's all I know."

"Yes, I was a German soldier. I never meant to be—I

never asked for this war."

Stefan paused to gather his thoughts. They were not simple, not easy to express. War had opened his eyes to the brutality of man. He had seen things he never wanted to see. He would never be the same. How would anyone ever understand?

"I went to war because I had to. I was called to duty, just like your son-in-law. It was not my choice. I left my home and family—my little girls—because I had to go. It was heartbreaking, leaving my family, our home. I felt torn in two. I had no idea that this war would be so terrible—that it would destroy villages, cities . . ."

Stefan stopped again. Looking back, thinking back, was overwhelming. He was not sure he wanted to go there. But he knew he had to.

"We had Jewish friends who disappeared. Are they dead? I don't know. Other friends were sent to Siberia to work. Will I ever see them again? My family had to leave our village because they were in danger. The Russians were coming. The Russians hate Germans. I have seen young girls raped, men beaten. Most of my friends from home are dead."

He leaned over and put his head in his hands. He took a few deep breaths. "I wonder—why am I alive? Why was I spared? There has to be a reason." Stefan looked over at Johann. Johann was quiet.

"Mama and Pop, Maria—they left everything. Our home, our land—we had to sell our store. I don't even know if Scheindorf is there anymore. Our family lived there for generations."

Johann listened. Stefan felt a little lighter with every word he spoke.

"All I have now is my family. I have nothing else. I

have no money, no property. What you have given me is shelter, and above all hope that I can stay alive to be with them again. Thank you—thank you for everything you have done for me. For your kindness."

Stefan's chest swelled with gratitude. His eyes filled with tears. This man had saved him.

Johann simply nodded. A moment later he said, "I would hope that a family might help Hans—as we have helped you."

Stefan paused for a moment and then continued, "Like most of us, I had high hopes for Germany. I wanted a stronger Germany. Hitler brought hope. But at what cost? I did not realize what was really going on until I saw it with my own eyes. Our country as we knew it is gone. The life we worked so hard to build is gone. It is never coming back."

Stefan looked down at his hands. Then he looked up at Johann.

"I do not believe in killing Jewish people. I do not believe in killing. I never did—I was forced to kill to stay alive." He remembered killing the woman sniper, burning villages and killing livestock. It had all been so wrong and so terrible.

They were both quiet for a moment.

"There are German soldiers, and then there are Nazis," Stefan went on. "Most of us in the German army, we were farmers, carpenters, roofers like you." Stefan looked down at his right hand and his missing trigger finger. "We built things, we grew crops, and we raised chickens and cows. We made wine and schnapps." He smiled for the first time. "We did not live to fight. We did not live for glory. We worked to make a life for our families. We worked hard like you do. In the field, they didn't tell us much. I didn't know where we were, what day it was—what was the plan—until the last minute when they told us."

Stefan looked out across the fields. Both men were quiet for a few minutes. "Before the war, when I was in the Romanian army—called into service like everyone else—I made a mistake, and a man nearly died. I realized then that I was responsible, even though I was ordered to do what I did. I was still responsible for my actions."

Stefan paused again. Playing the accordion flashed into his head. He wondered if he would ever play again. Could he?

"In this war—I was not innocent. We are all part of the collective guilt. Those of us who went to war, though we were not Nazis, we did not lead this campaign, we are still guilty. Whether we fought, or gave up our Jewish neighbors to the Nazis, or just stood by and let things happen—we should feel the pain of this war."

He stopped to glance over again at Johann. Johann was looking out over the golden wheat waving in the wind, rocking in his chair.

"In the field, I saw men forget the Ten Commandments. Men killed, raped women, stole whatever they needed. We lost our morality. Men acted without a conscience. It is unbearable to think about this—how the rules we would never break in our daily lives were suddenly okay to break. How is that possible? The truth is not simple, you know? I know you must believe this because you took me in—knowing I had been a German soldier."

Johann looked over at him with a serious expression. "All people are different. All people think differently. Why would I think all German soldiers were the same?"

Relief flooded through Stefan at the simple answer. Johann understood.

Johann continued, "We were all naïve. We did not see this coming. No one could have predicted this—this crime against humanity. This violation. This destruction of life and property." He stopped rocking. "We believed Hitler's promises, like all Germans. The children who died—the girls who were raped—families will never be the same again. The consequences of this war will haunt Germany forever."

Johann looked at Stefan. "You are alive for a reason. God has protected you. You have a purpose in life, a family who needs you—not just to be their provider, but to set an example, to teach your children. You have learned from this war. You are a man who has now seen how bad man can be—how low we can stoop. One by one, each person can make a difference. Make that difference, Stefan."

The sun had set. Stefan could no longer see Johann's face, but his growing trust in the man beside him kept him talking.

"The Americans—we declared war on them. My father always said if the Americans got involved in a war, like they did in the Great War, that we would lose. I don't believe that all Americans are alike, either. I don't know any Americans, and I didn't fight any Americans, but I feel that I know a little bit about America because both of my parents lived there."

"They did?" Johann asked, suddenly animated. "What was it like? Why are they here now?"

"It's a long story." Stefan smiled. "For another night. But let me tell you—they have wanted to go back to America since I was born."

Stefan looked out into the darkness. The night noises of summer got louder, and the light of fireflies flickered. His heart felt lighter for the first time in months.

"Pop wanted it for all of us. They both loved America. Even though they worked so hard there, they wanted to go back. Maybe, someday, God willing—we will."

CHAPTER NINETEEN

*"To what extent can the obviously simple peasants
who troop to church on Sunday morning in decent black
be responsible for the horrors of the Nazis?"*
George Orwell

Plauen, Germany
Summer 1945

WITHIN DAYS OF Stefan's heartfelt conversation with
Johann, American soldiers came. They rounded up the
German soldiers in the area and loaded them into big
transport trucks, a hundred or so men to a truck, and
drove them to the POW camp in Jägersgrün, east of
Plauen, in Russian-occupied Germany. Stefan got off
the truck with the other prisoners. The camp, surrounded
by a tall barbed-wire fence, was in a huge pasture in a
valley. There were hundreds of soldiers already there.
The grass, as far as he could see, was green and lush.

Stefan walked through the sea of soldiers milling
around, searching for someone he might know, and trying
to find out what was going to happen. He had hoped he
would be going home. Why were they being held? The
war was over. Many of the men were sick, malnourished,

wounded, or delirious. Stefan was in better shape than most—he had Johann and his family to thank for that. He had had several weeks of food and shelter, much more than most of the men in the camp. He was once again grateful.

For two days, there was no food. Each day, hundreds of soldiers entered the camp. Tents for medical assistance and food were set up. Soon there were thousands of soldiers crowded into the area, but there were few sleeping tents except those for the Americans, no latrines, and not enough food to go around. Men slept on the ground without blankets. When it rained, they slept in puddles of water. The dead piled up, and the stench was overpowering. Stefan and other soldiers helped carry the dead to the perimeter of the camp. By the end of the week, the verdant field had turned into a lake of mud.

After a few days, American officers arrived. They set up a tent. Armed American soldiers herded the German soldiers, about a hundred at a time, to the tent where they stood outside in a long line. Stefan's turn came, and he fell into line. He was not sure where the line went or what would happen.

Finally, he was at the front of the line. He entered the tent. A table was set up in the center. Three officers sat at the table. An armed guard stood by.

One of the officers motioned for Stefan to come forward to his station.

"Is there anything wrong with you?" an American officer asked.

"No," Stefan responded.

"Can you work?"

"Yes."

Stefan was not sure if it was the smart thing to do,

but he told the truth. Sent to another area and assigned to a tent, he did not know what would happen next. He was sitting outside of the tent when a man came up. The man was giddy—smiling and laughing. Stefan thought that perhaps he had lost his mind.

"So what's with you?" Stefan asked.

"I'm going home!"

Stefan smiled, taken in by the man's joy. Someone was going home. Someday he would too.

"Where's home?"

"Austria," the man answered.

Stefan was suddenly very interested.

"Where in Austria?"

"Linz."

"Do you live in Linz?"

"No, I live in Altmünster, not far from Linz."

Stefan could not believe it. He stood up. Could this be true? Would this man give a message to Maria? He had to be certain. "Do you know the people who lived next to the school?" Stefan asked.

"Yes. His name is Hessenberger, and he makes wine drums."

"Now I believe," Stefan said. A sudden lump in his throat made it hard to speak. He could get word to his family!

"You think I didn't tell you the truth?"

"It is hard to know who to trust these days," Stefan said. "What's your name?"

"Martin."

Stefan swallowed his joy. "Martin, I'm going to trust you. Would you do me a favor? It would mean a great deal to me and my family."

Martin seemed too happy to turn anyone down.

"Sure, why not. What's the favor?"

"My wife, my children, and my parents are in Alt-münster, in the school near the Hessenbergers. Her name is Maria. Would you tell my wife that you saw me? My name is Stefan. Tell her about my missing trigger finger, and she will believe you. Tell her that I hope to follow you home soon."

———

Altmünster, Austria
1945

Maria walked home from church, as she did every morning before she started her work. The day was already warm. She slipped off her blue babushka and ran her fingers through her long hair. She would twist it into a knot and pin it up before she started cleaning houses.

The brief walk alone gave her time to feel the pain of Stefan's absence—the emptiness that seeped into her bones, making her weary. A part of her was missing. He was on her mind constantly. At night, her loneliness surfaced in full force. She struggled to remember what it felt like, his warm body next to hers, being sheltered in his strong arms.

She prayed to God to protect him and bring him home. She prayed to St. Anthony. *St. Anthony, I promise that if you bring Stefan home safe that I will put a statue of you in our home. I promise.* She remembered what Stefan had said to her, "Live day by day, take care of the girls, and God will provide." *St. Anthony of Padua, pray for us.* Today was the ninth day of her nine-day novena.

The family was fine. While she worked, Gertrude took care of the house and watched Siglinda. Every week Maria saved a little money, thinking she could buy Stefan an accordion someday. Opa ran errands and delivered supplies using the wagon. It was nearly Siglinda's fourth birthday, and Gertrude had been secretly busy making doll clothes from leftover cloth. Klothilde was growing tall; at seven, she was in school. They were crowded into a two-room apartment in Altmünster, but they had a roof over their heads, and they were safe. With everyone helping, they had enough food and the essentials of life.

Maria went into their apartment and closed the door. She put her rosary by the small statue of St. Anthony, as was her custom. She was surprised to hear a knock on the door behind her.

"Who is it?" Gertrude asked as she walked into the room holding Siglinda by the hand.

"I don't know," Maria said. "I just got home."

"Be careful," Gertrude said.

"Who is it, Oma?" Siglinda asked Gertrude. "Mutti, who is it?"

"Siglinda, go back," Gertrude said, guiding the little one back to safety. "Stay in there. Just a minute!" She closed the door to the sleeping room.

When Siglinda was out of sight, Maria, with Gertrude standing close behind her, opened the door a crack and peered out.

A man she had never seen before stood there. She was immediately on guard.

"Are you Stefan's wife—the Stefan with the missing trigger finger?"

Maria's heart raced at the mention of her husband. Caution aside, she opened the door and looked at the man. She had to know. Her eyes filled with tears. "What do you want?"

"He wanted me to find you."

Maria felt faint. She was starved for news. He was alive!

"Where did you see him?" she asked.

"I saw him in Jägersgrün, outside of Plauen. He is in an American POW camp, but it could be Russian now. He was alive when I left—weeks ago."

"He's alive!" Gertrude said loudly.

"Thank you, God!" Maria said. She turned to Gertrude and both women wrapped their arms around each other.

———•———

Once a beautiful city, Plauen, as far as he could see, was a shell of crushed buildings, completely devastated by the bombings. People lived among piles of rubble, finding shelter where they could in collapsed and burnt-out structures or underground. The roads were crumbling and cratered. The magnificent trees that once bordered the streets were black and skeletal. Parks, once lush, green oases, were brown and dusty.

Stefan, like most of the prisoners, worked clearing debris. The work was hard, but he was used to hard work. What made it heartbreaking was watching the people suffer. Most were homeless, and many were sick. He watched orphaned children wander alone, drinking from puddles of water in the street, their faces smudged with dirt. Cities had lost their water supply, sewage pipes were broken, and there was no electricity. He could not imagine what winter would do to these people, so unprepared, with no heat, clean water, or shelter, and with only limited food. The repercussions of the war touched every family. War continued to kill even after it ended.

The rations in the camp were meager, and prisoners starved to death. Stefan had never dreamed that he would be a prisoner, forced to work for the Americans after the war was over. He followed orders, thought of the man who had gone home to Austria, and hoped that his own release would come soon.

One morning when Stefan awoke, the Americans were gone. Their medical tent, the camp kitchen, and all of the facilities for sanitation and clean water were gone. The Russians had taken over.

An armed Russian soldier came into his tent. "Do not try to escape. If you try, we will shoot you on sight. When we say so, we will give you a piece of paper and you will go home."

Two weeks passed. Daily rations, cut to a bowl of watery soup and a piece of bread, were not enough to sustain the men. Deaths mounted as illness and starvation picked them off. The prisoners were told to get ready for a march when their names were called. The Russians started calling names. They called names for days and days. Stefan waited for them to call his. *I will find them*, he told himself. Hundreds of men in the camp died every day. More men fell sick with dysentery and fever. The dead piled up, and the prisoners buried them in mass graves.

It was unbearable, the stench, the hunger, the sadness.

Stefan finished carrying a dead man to a mass grave. He was exhausted and discouraged. He dropped to his knees and prayed. *Please God, please call my name! My family needs me. I need them!*

Days went by, and one day, Stefan heard a name called that he recognized—Stefan Funkenhauser, a friend from Scheindorf. He was elated. Energy flooded his body—*to see a friendly face!* He ran to find Stefan, but his friend was nowhere. He had been taken away too quickly. He fought back the bitter disappointment. Later, he heard that the men were taken to labor camps in Siberia, not released. If that were true, he would never see his friend again.

When there were still some ten thousand men in the camp, the Russians announced that everyone was going on a march. They were going to the Americans in Hof, Germany, some fifty kilometers away. The prisoners were rounded up, and Stefan fell in line, hopeful that the Americans would have food and shelter, that in this new camp, they might be treated like human beings, and that he would be released.

Along the way to Hof, many men died. The German soldiers walked alone or in small clusters, supporting the weak, but it was not enough to save everyone. The Russians shot those who stumbled and fell, and lacked the strength to get up. They were left on the side of the road.

When they reached Hof, Stefan was surprised to see that compared to the devastation of Plauen; the city was in much better shape. There were bombed-out buildings and streets pocked with black holes from shelling, and debris was everywhere, but there were many buildings intact.

He learned it was July 26. He had missed Siglinda's birthday. Stefan sat on a stump near the rail yard, weak and delirious from the long march with no food or drink. He let his mind drift back in time—to a happier time, a lifetime ago, to four years ago—remembering Maria, heavy with child, working in the fields and going into labor. How he had walked her home, her contractions stopping them along the way. Then little Siglinda, in a hurry to be born, slipping out of her mutti on the kitchen floor! They were so happy with their new baby. They had had no idea what was ahead. Probably just as well not to know the future.

Stefan kept his memories close; they surfaced often to comfort him. "I love you, Maria," he whispered. Regardless of where he was, he knew where he was going—to find Maria.

Nuremberg, Germany
1945

In Hof, American soldiers loaded Stefan with thousands of other German soldiers into cattle cars and locked the doors. The hot and smelly cars, caked with animal waste, were their holding pen for two days. Stefan's hopes that the Americans would treat them better slipped away. It was standing room only. There was no food or water. The heat was unbearable. Men suffocated. Stefan was standing near an outside wall, so he could breathe through the holes in the sides. He helped other men to get a whiff of fresh air.

As the days passed, Stefan thought of the German soldiers, his friend Stefan Funkenhauser, loaded into cattle cars by the Russians and transported to Siberia. Were the Jews, taken from their homes, separated from their families, treated this way? He felt the anger of the Americans for what Germany had done. Men were dying all around him. This was not an accident; it was punishment. He prayed to live.

Finally, the car started to move. The train traveled less than a day and stopped. The doors to the cattle car slid open. The sunlight was blinding. Stefan covered his eyes with his arm. Fresh air rushed in. He took deep gulps of it, feeling the life it gave him, and exhaling the poisonous fumes he had been breathing for days. Armed American soldiers, bandanas covering their noses and mouths, motioned with their guns for the prisoners to get out of the car.

It was Stefan's turn to leave. He sat on the edge of the car and finally jumped to the ground. His weak legs trembled, barely able to support him. He was no longer the strong man he had always been. He looked out and saw long lines of men splashing and drinking water from animal troughs. He stumbled toward an empty space beside a trough, plunged his head in, and greedily drank. The water was brown, but that did not matter. It was wet. He needed water to survive.

Someone said they were in Nuremberg.

Thousands of German soldiers were loaded onto waiting American trucks for the twelve-kilometer trip to the POW camp. Since there were not enough trucks, Stefan and scores of others walked alongside the convoy. Men fell to their knees, unable to walk any further. The Americans picked them up and loaded them on the already overfilled trucks.

This time, the camp was nothing more than a huge field with a covered pavilion. There were no tents set up for shelter. The prisoners, frail from lack of food and water, were ordered to dig holes for their three-man tents and pitch them. The men assigned to Stefan's tent dug a trench on the inside so they could sit with their feet hanging over the side. Then they made a sleeping pallet by covering the ground with fallen leaves and straw. The two men who shared his tent all had stories to tell about the war. Each of them wanted to go home. Ben was from Bonn and Gerard from Berlin.

The next day, Stefan and thousands of other German soldiers who were able to work climbed into trucks that held about a hundred prisoners each, along with ten American guards. They traveled to the city of Nuremberg to their work detail. The once beautiful city was now a shelled-out crater of crumbled buildings, burned centuries old trees stripped of their leaves, and homeless, starving residents. The residents, mostly women, children, and the elderly, were living underground.

As they entered the city, Stefan saw a woman who had built a fire under a piece of sheet metal. The metal was hot, and she was cooking something on top of it in a pot. The scenes of destruction were impossible to comprehend. Was there anyone who was not touched by the war? He did not think so.

Stefan and the other prisoners spent all day cleaning debris and loading it into trucks. They hauled bricks, concrete chunks, and shattered beams of wood, clearing and sweeping streets. The guards surrounded the prisoners, smoking and taunting them by tossing their lit cigarettes at the prisoner's feet. Stefan would have loved a smoke, but there was no way he would pick up a cigarette. No one would—not while the soldiers watched. When they turned their back, that was another matter.

One day a woman, stooped and gray, wearing a black

shawl, quietly found her way around the American guards. She motioned to the German soldiers—*Come here!* She put a finger to her lips—*Quiet*. She had a bucket of water and some loaves of bread. Out of sight, she offered them ladles of fresh rainwater. Stefan thought he had never tasted anything so good. They shared the bread, quickly stuffing it into their mouths and swallowing before they were caught. They had not been so lucky before. Other times, when civilians had offered them food, the guards had tossed the food and water into the street.

One evening, Stefan, Ben, and Gerard were talking quietly in their tent. It had been another day of the never-ending cleanup of Nuremberg. They were starving. Darkness was falling. Stefan pulled three half-smoked cigarettes, secretly pocketed during the day, and passed them out.

"Do you hear the soldiers talking?" Ben asked.

"Sometimes," Stefan said.

"I do," Gerard said. "Today I heard why there is so much going on here. All of these trucks arriving with civilians. There are hundreds of them here—Americans and British—maybe Russian too."

"I've heard talk of war crimes and trials," Ben said.

"They're looking for the Nazis—the ones who planned the war," Gerard said.

Stefan was alarmed. "Are we here because of this? Are we going to be tried?"

"I don't know," Ben said.

"I did not want this war—I had no part of planning. I was in the army because I had to be. I had no choice," Stefan said. "I can't believe they will put us on trial!"

"What I heard was only bits and pieces," Gerard

said. "But I'm pretty sure I heard them say that civilians and soldiers could be charged—and something about killing Jews."

Ben hung his head and then spoke quietly. "At the camp before this one, we were all herded into a building and shown a film." He stopped. "The Americans showed us a film of a German concentration camp. We were forced to watch. We saw the piles of bodies, the mutilation in operating rooms, the showers, and gas chambers. It was the most horrible thing I ever saw. I covered my eyes during parts of it. Some of the men started crying."

Ben took a deep breath. "We did this. Our leaders ordered this."

"I knew of it," Stefan said. "I heard about it on the way to Babruysk. I overheard Nazi officers talking."

"I didn't have anything to do with that," Ben said. "Never."

"None of us here did—but others did. They are crimes—crimes by the German people," Gerard said. "I heard that they are screening thousands of people to determine who is responsible. And . . ." He looked at his friends and said soberly, "they will be punished."

"And that's happening here, in Nuremberg?" Stefan asked.

Gerard nodded. "Everything is happening in the Palace of Justice—because it's almost in one piece. They are fixing it up for the trials."

Gerard looked down at his hands. "It is ironic that Germans will be tried in our own Palace of Justice, in the city of so many Nazi Party events." He looked up at his tent mates. "Isn't it?"

There was silence for a moment.

Their cigarettes smoked, it was now dark in the tent.

"I think they plan to teach us a lesson," Ben said.

That night Stefan lay awake and worried about what that could mean.

CHAPTER TWENTY

"Dates of destiny are always on time."
Anonymous

Nuremberg, Germany
Fall 1945

ONE DAY AFTER several weeks of cleanup duty in Nuremberg, Stefan found himself in the POW camp waiting in line with hundreds of German soldiers. He was next to be interrogated by American "judges." He was anxious. He did not know what to expect. The only information he heard was through the camp grapevine. Evidently, there were about twenty-five different judges, and they all spoke perfect German. What would they want? What would they do?

He had come so far. The war was over. He felt trapped in this zone of uncertainty.

It was his turn. His heart was hammering. He walked through the tent entrance and saw a long table with three men in uniform. There was a single chair before the tribunal.

The officer in the center finished his cigarette, rubbed in out in an ashtray full of butts, and motioned for Stefan to take the chair. He was a little older than Stefan, dark-haired and physically fit. He sat at attention and did not introduce himself or the other two men.

The two men did not speak. One man wrote in his notebook. He did not even look up when Stefan entered. The other man gave Stefan a long, suspicious look that pierced right through him.

"Let us begin," the judge said in German.

Stefan nodded. *Just get through this* ran through his mind.

"Where were you born?"

"Scheindorf, in Hungary/Romania."

"Which is it, Hungary or Romania?" the officer asked impatiently.

"When I was born, Scheindorf was in Hungary. When my first daughter was born, it was Romania. Last I heard it was Hungary again. Borders change."

"When did you join the German army?"

"I was conscripted and entered the army on March 27, 1942."

"What was your rank?"

"Senior lance corporal."

"What company?"

Stefan told them. He sat up straight, on alert, watching for clues from the facial expressions of the men who sat behind the table.

"Where did you fight?"

"Mostly in Russia." Stefan put his hands together and hoped they might notice he had lost his trigger finger.

"What were your duties?"

"At first, it was finding Russian partisans."

"How long?"

"Months. I really don't remember dates or even know

some of the locations. We were given little information, only told what to do. We were constantly on the move."

The men wrote in their notebooks. Stefan was sweating. He could read nothing from the men's expressions—nothing about their thoughts or intentions.

"Then later?"

"We were at the front. I lost my trigger finger near Stalingrad." Stefan held up his hand.

"Who were you fighting?"

"Russian soldiers."

"Are you sure?"

"Yes, sir."

"What did you do after that?"

"I ran supplies, ammo—in the field."

"That's it?"

Stefan felt the judge did not believe him. What more could he say to convince him?

"I drove trucks and trained new recruits."

All three men stared at him now—their looks penetrating.

"Did you ever fight Americans?"

"No, sir."

"You positive about that?"

"I never fought Americans." He was relieved he could tell the truth about that.

The judge leaned over to the man on his right, whispered something, and the man nodded.

"That's all for today," the judge said. "You're dismissed."

Stefan took a deep breath and stood up.

"Thank you, sir," he said. Being polite could not hurt. Stefan could hardly wait to get out of there.

As the weeks went by, Stefan was summoned routinely for interviews by diverse panels of judges. Though how the questions were asked varied, and they might be in a different order, they were always the same. He gave them the same answers—the truth.

Stefan found an extra job—washing socks and underwear for the Americans. They would give him food or a few cigarettes in payment. He was so hungry he would not only eat the orange but the entire peel—it tasted so good. Hunger haunted him day and night. His clothes, caked with sweat and dirt, hung on his lean frame.

One day Stefan discovered that the Americans were looking for prisoners to work in the American dining room in Nuremberg. It was a far better job than the filthy and backbreaking work of cleaning up debris in the streets and buildings of the city. He volunteered.

While driving into Nuremberg with other volunteers and American soldiers, he worried about his family. Had Maria received the news that he was alive? Were they still in Altmünster? He was sure the girls were growing. He ached with longing for them. It was hard not to be discouraged. This was taking so long. The days had blurred into weeks, and he was going nowhere. When would he be released? *Would* they release him? Waiting was agony.

They approached a large compound buzzing with activity. Trucks and jeeps were coming and going. Men in suits and soldiers in uniform swarmed the area. Once in the building, he and five other volunteers were guided to the dining room. An American cook, his German limited, explained to them in words and hand motions that they would be responsible for cleaning up after meals. Stefan was just fine with that. He would be around food.

An officer stepped in after the cook finished explaining their duties. He was tall and broad-shouldered. He spoke to them sternly in German. "You are not to take food from plates or from the table. If you are caught, you will be punished. You will be reassigned another duty. And it will not involve food. You will be painting, cleaning latrines, or hauling debris. Understood?"

Stefan and the others nodded.

"But you can take cigars, cigarettes, pipes, cigarette holders, matches, lighters, chocolate, and other candy— nothing else," the officer said. "Just no food." He looked around to see if everyone understood. "All you have to do is clear the dishes, take the dishes and utensils and any leftover food, and load it on the dumbwaiter. It will go down to the dishwashers." The officer paused. "When the dining room is cleared, you may go to the kitchen, and you will eat the same food we eat—whatever is left."

This was the best news Stefan had heard in months. He could hardly believe it.

Stefan came every day and worked tables. Every night, he returned to his tent with a box of leftover cigars, cigarettes, and candy to share. Most nights, he was able to bring back two buckets of good food from the kitchen. In the morning, he brought the empty pails back. The job was a dream come true. He had one problem solved—his hunger—and he was gaining his strength back.

———— • ————

Once again, he was called to be questioned before the judges. Stefan shook his head as he entered the tent.

The routine was familiar. He nodded to the judge in the center, a man about his age, and took a seat facing the three men behind the table.

"What is your name?" the judge began, speaking perfect German. The man's accent reminded Stefan of home.

"My name is Stefan Revak."

"When were you born?"

"December 18, 1914."

"Where were you born?"

"In Scheindorf, Hungary/Romania."

The judge paused. He appeared to be thinking.

"Revak . . . Revak," he said to himself as if trying to remember something.

Then he started asking the list of questions: Where were you fighting? What was your company? Were you in this country? Were you in Russia?

"Did you fight against the Americans?"

"I was in the infantry, and I never fought against the Americans."

"When you were with the Panzers, you were fighting the Americans, no?"

"No, I did not say that. I wasn't with the Panzers."

"But you wear a Panzer uniform."

"My uniform was stolen. This was all I could find to wear."

The judge kept at Stefan, trying to catch him in a lie.

After continuous questioning, the judge paused and looked down at the paper in front of him. Once again, he said, "Revak . . ." He started to move the paperweight on his desk around, then the cup of pencils. He appeared deep in thought. He looked up and locked eyes with

Stefan.

"Stefan, do you have relatives in the US?"

This question was new. Stefan tried not to let his surprise show. "Yes."

"Do you know them?"

"No."

"How come you don't know them?"

"They left for America before I was born."

"Do you know their names?"

"Yes, Mr. and Mrs. Treer and Mr. and Mrs. Pfitzner. Three of my father's brothers are also there."

Stefan could sense the judge was suddenly very interested. This was more than the usual questioning.

"Do you know Mr. and Mrs. Pfitzner?"

"No, I told you. I never met them. They went to America before I was born."

The judge paused again, and he twirled his pencil around in his hand.

"Do you want to go to America too?"

Stefan was surprised by the question, but he responded quickly. "Sir, look at me. Look where we are. How could I even think of that? I don't even know where my family is right now."

The judge frowned and looked down again. Then he looked up at Stefan. "Wait a minute. Wasn't someone from your immediate family in America?"

"Yes, my mother was there from 1910 to 1914. She came home and married my father. Then my father was in America from 1920 to 1925."

"Where?"

"In Passaic, New Jersey. My father worked there. He wanted my mother and me to come to America, to be together as a family, but it never worked out."

"Where is your father now?"

"I don't know. The last time I saw him was in Alt-münster, Austria."

"So he left America?"

"Yes, when my mother and I were unable to come to America, he came back to Scheindorf."

The judge paused, and his brow furrowed.

"How is the Pfitzner family related to you?"

"Mrs. Pfitzner is my aunt. She is my mother's sister."

The judge looked puzzled. Stefan had no idea where this conversation was going.

"Was your father a strong man?"

"Yes, he's always been a strong man."

"Did he learn to speak English?"

"He had a hard time with it," Stefan said. By now, he was completely bewildered.

Stefan saw a small smile slip across the judge's face. What was going on here?

"Do you have a cousin named Helen?"

Stefan sat forward, shocked. How did this American know so much about his family? "Yes, Helen Pfitzner."

The judge sat back, triumphant, as though he had just solved a mystery. "I think I knew your father."

Stefan could not believe what he was hearing.

"I used to go on walks with Helen and your father—many times. Your father helped me learn German. I tried to help him speak English. You are right—he did have trouble."

Stefan's heart started to beat rapidly.

The judge put down his pencil and sat back in his chair for a moment. All was silent in the room. Then he leaned forward, looked into Stefan's eyes, and spoke.

"Soon you will leave and go find your wife and children. And then you will go to America."

CHAPTER TWENTY-ONE

*"And one by one
the nights between our separated cities
are joined to the night that unites us."*
Pablo Neruda

Nuremberg, Germany
Late Fall, 1945

AFTER THAT CONVERSATION, Stefan waited with renewed hope for news of his release. Nothing happened. He continued to work in the American dining room as well as do laundry for American soldiers. He was able to keep his tent mates supplied with both food and smokes. He was no longer starving, and he had a decent "job," but he was no closer to going home.

Called before an endless parade of judges, always probing him with their questions, he never again saw the American judge who knew his father. Stefan wished he could have been bold enough to ask the judge questions of his own. *Was this just talk, what he said about going to America?* Stefan could not stop thinking about what Isabelle had said to him in Saxony when she told his fortune: "You will cross a big body of water."

Stefan got up as usual at 4 a.m. and was on his way to take the truck to work when he heard his name called. He was directed to a workstation in the camp. Filled with apprehension, he wondered what he might have done wrong.

He walked into the office. An American soldier looked up from his paperwork. Stefan introduced himself.

The soldier rifled through his papers.

"I think I know how this comes out," he said. "How come you're going home?"

Stefan could not believe it. The soldier told him to go back to his tent, pack his things, and find someone to replace him in the dining room. An American officer would come for him.

Stefan had just returned to his tent when a black limousine pulled up. An American officer got out and told him to go ahead and pack—they would wait for him. Stefan quickly packed his few possessions and stuffed as many cigarettes as he could carry into a sack. He was back at the car as fast as he could go.

Stefan sat in the back seat with the American officer. They drove for hours past Nuremberg, hundreds of kilometers to Anspach, Germany. When they stopped, Stefan looked out the car window, and his heart fell. It was another camp. There were no tents, just sheds with roofs. He got out of the car. This was worse than Nuremberg. He could see it right away. Many of the men milling around were sick and malnourished. The men were from everywhere—Hungary, Germany, Romania.

Assigned to a shed, he walked in. There was nothing in the shed but straw and a man with a very bad cough. The man coughed and spit up blood into a dirty rag, then looked up at him with dark eyes crusted with matter.

What have I done to deserve this?

Later that afternoon, Stefan heard his name called once more. He was taken to a large building and told to report to an office on the second floor. He walked up the stairs and found the office. He knocked on the door.

"Come in," a voice said.

Stefan opened the door and walked in. A man sat at a desk, going through some papers. He looked up from his work and smiled. Stefan recognized him immediately: the American judge who knew his father. He did not know what to think. Was this another test?

"So Stefan, what did I tell you?"

"We talked a long time ago. I thought it would be a few days."

"No—things don't work that fast around here." The judge leaned back in his chair. "How many guys got out from where you were?"

"None," Stefan said.

"See?" the judge shrugged his shoulders. "And you are here."

"You know, I don't even know your name," Stefan said.

The man behind the desk stood.

"Captain Thomas Wiehl," he said. He reached out his hand to shake Stefan's. "Glad our paths crossed. Your father was a good man."

———·+·———

Stefan began the tedious exit process, going from

one office to another. Once cleared by a German physician, he was told to go back to his shed and wait for transportation to Austria. He waited all day, then another, then another. He was finished with waiting. He had been patient long enough. On the fourth day, he walked back Captain Wiehl's building. He saw him outside, heading toward the building.

"Captain Wiehl!" Stefan called out.

The American officer stopped and turned around. He looked surprised. "Stefan, are you still here?"

"Yes, they told me to wait for transport. That was three days ago."

"I'll take care of it," Captain Wiehl said. "It takes forever to get anything done around here—military red tape."

The officer headed back toward his office and Stefan toward his quarters.

"Hey, Stefan," Captain Wiehl called.

Stefan turned. "Yes?"

"Tell your father I said hello, will you? He was the one who taught me the most German, you know."

"I didn't know," Stefan said. "But it shows. You speak his dialect—with his accent." Stefan smiled for the first time in months.

As he walked back to the shed Stefan thought, *Pop will never believe this story!* He could not wait to tell him.

Not ten minutes had gone by when Stefan heard his name called, along with another man by the name of Albert. Two men were waiting for them with a civilian car. They put their belongings in the trunk, and everyone got in. All Stefan could think about was finding Maria.

The men drove just outside of Breslau and stopped the car.

"Out of the car," one of them said.

Stefan and Albert looked at one another, unsure of what this meant.

"We've got business here," the driver said.

"Yeah, the girls are waiting," the other man said. "Get out."

They unloaded Stefan and Albert's belongings from the trunk and dropped them on the side of the road.

"Here are your papers. You are free now. Go on—get out of here!"

The two men got back into the car and drove away, leaving Stefan and Albert in the middle of the road. Stefan was stunned.

"What do we do now?" Albert said.

Stefan scanned the area, trying to figure out what to do next. He pointed to a building about a quarter-mile away. "Looks like a train station over there." He craned his neck to see. "The bridge is out."

"I hear a train," Albert said. "Hear it—in the distance?"

"There's got to be a temporary bridge," Stefan said. "Let's go!"

They ran like wild men to catch the train. When they reached the other side of the bridge, they stopped short—border patrol. They walked cautiously toward the soldiers.

"Passports?" The guard reached out his hand to Albert.

Albert gave the guard his papers. He was Austrian and allowed to pass.

"Passport," the guard said to Stefan. Stefan gave him his papers.

The guard roughly pushed them back at Stefan. "I

need your passport."

"I don't have it. I just got out of camp today."

"Go back," the soldier pointed. "There is the front line *stalag*. When it opens in the morning, get in line and give them your papers. When you get your passport, come back."

Stefan said good-bye to Albert. Depressed, he walked down the road slowly. Was he ever going to get to his family? He had passed every test and still he was not free. Night was falling. He saw a man down the way, sitting on the side of the road. The man had made a rough camp with straw, his jacket for a pillow. As Stefan approached, the man looked up at Stefan and nodded. Stefan stopped and told the man his story.

"Sit down. Nothing to do until the morning. You'll figure it out," the man said.

Stefan sat down next to him. He put his head in his hands. Home had been so close he could almost touch it, and then it was snatched away from him—like waking up suddenly from a good dream.

The man shared his food with Stefan and offered him some apple wine. Stefan's heart warmed toward the stranger. He doubted he would ever see this man again, and he could certainly never repay him. How could this man be so kind—sharing his meager provisions?

Stefan ate slowly. It was his first taste of wine in months. It tasted golden, like the best of harvest. His mind drifted back to working with Uncle Anton as a boy, mashing the apples, making wine. *Did that ever happen?* All his recent memories were of hunger, cold, and pain; loss and sickness; the smell of gunpowder, smoke, and death. His past seemed modest and happy, even though it had been a lot of work and marked by life's usual growing pains. It was so long ago. In war, he lived day by day, staying alive only because he had someone to love.

The crisp, sweet taste of the wine flooded him with thoughts of harvest, the rich smell of the earth, and the crush of fruit. He thought of the festivals, singing and dancing with beautiful Maria, her laughing eyes only for him. He thought of playing the accordion in the cool fall evenings. They had been such simple, joyful pleasures. Was that all gone now?

Stefan spent that first night of freedom near the side of the road with a man he had never met—a man he would never forget. When the sun came, he got ready to head to the border stalag.

"I can never repay you," he said.

"Pray for me," the man said. "That I get home too."

"I will."

As Stefan approached the border station, he was shocked to see over one hundred men waiting in line for their papers. He approached one of the men.

"How long have you been waiting?" Stefan asked.

"Ten days."

Stefan was stunned. This could not be. Surely, it would not take so long.

He approached another man, further up the line.

"How long have you been waiting?"

"Seven days."

Stefan went into the building and passed through a long corridor with many windows for processing. He spotted a man at the window. There was no line in front of the man. He approached with a hope born of desperation.

"I need a passport to go over the border," he said.

"Do you have your separation papers?"

Stefan unbuttoned his worn tunic to remove them, and the man at the window saw his cigarettes. He turned around and called to another man. "Josef, do you have a cigarette?"

"No, I don't," replied Josef.

Stefan caught on quickly.

He offered the man a cigarette. Then Stefan thought better and gave him the entire pack.

"Give me your papers," the man said. "Wait here." He turned around and left the window.

The man returned about ten minutes later.

"Here you go." He slid the documents toward Stefan. "Here's your passport."

Stefan could not believe it. He thanked the man, carefully pocketed the passport, and headed to the border.

Stefan passed through the border patrol without a problem. At the train station, he planned to take a train to Linz and then Altmünster. He did not know where his family was—if they were back in Hungary, or still in Altmünster, or somewhere else entirely. But he was free and he would find them, no matter how long it took. Altmünster was the place to start.

When the train from Linz was nearing the station where he would have to switch trains, he overheard two women talking about Altmünster.

"Are the Hungarian refugees still there?" he asked.

"No, they left right after the war ended," one of the women replied.

What to do now? His mind raced, but he decided to stick to his original plan. He would go on to Altmünster and talk with the mayor or someone in authority who could give him an idea of what direction his family had traveled. Perhaps, too, Maria would have left word for him.

When he arrived in Altmünster, it was dark and late, about ten o'clock. He had no idea where he would stay. He looked out the window of the train, and in the dim light of the station, he saw a familiar form. He strained into the dimness—yes, he knew this woman! It was his cousin, Margaret Maria, standing there. He got off the train and walked up to her, crushing her in his arms. "You're still here!" Stefan said. "You're still here!"

Margaret Maria was so surprised, all she could say was, "Mar, Mar"—she could not even say Maria.

"Is Maria still here? Mama and Pop?"

"Yes," his cousin said, patting her heart, taking a deep breath, trying to recover from the shock of seeing him. After a moment, she quickly caught him up. Margaret Maria and her brother Philip were still in the *schloss*, an abandoned castle. Since it was late, Margaret Maria took him home, and he talked with them until about 11:00 p.m. They shared what food they had with him. They had so much to talk about, but he wanted to go home.

"It's dark and a little confusing to get there," Philip said. "It will be easier if I walk you there."

Stefan could not believe it was finally happening. He was going to see his family. He was no longer tired—no longer hungry.

They walked to the apartment Maria and the girls shared with his parents. Philip knocked on the door.

"Get up. Maria—it's Philip! Maria!" He knocked loudly on the door. "Maria!"

To Stefan, the moments he waited seemed like hours. After a few minutes, the door opened.

Stefan thought he was seeing an angel. Maria, wearing a long white flannel nightgown and a black wool shawl, carried a lighted candle that softly illuminated her face. Her curly dark hair cascaded to her shoulders.

"Philip—what's going on? Is everything all right?"

She looked beyond Philip and saw Stefan.

Stefan watched her eyes go wide with surprise, then fill with tears.

She dropped the candle.

He rushed to her and wrapped her in his arms, holding her tight. He had never felt or smelled anything so good. He would never let her go again. He covered her head with kisses. Tears slipped down his face.

She pulled away from him and looked into his eyes. Her gaze shifted from shock and disbelief to deep awareness. A sense of peace settled over them both. Her eyes shone with love, and her smile was contagious. He could not believe that they were finally together.

"Stefan, I just finished a nine-day novena today. And you are home!"

PART V

CHAPTER TWENTY-TWO

"The great thing in this world
is not so much where you stand,
as in what direction you are moving."
Oliver Wendell Holmes

Winter 1945 to December 31, 1946
Altmünster to Neunkirchen to Losenstein, Austria;
Altusried, Germany

MARIA SLEPT LITTLE during that night. She watched
him breathe. She traced her fingers around his face, his
lean jawline, felt the stubble of his beard and the turn of
his mouth. He did not move. She had waited for this
moment for years. He was home. All through the months
of his absence, she had been certain he was alive—as
sure as she was of the beat of her heart. Yet she did not
trust her heart to protect him. She had needed God's
help. He had answered her prayers.

The girls slept through his arrival. They would be
surprised to see him. She was sure Siglinda would not
know him and would need gentle coaxing to build trust
in the stranger who was her father.

Maria dozed on and off, and when she awoke before

dawn, she could not move. Stefan's arm was wrapped tight as a vise around her. She had to get up—find some food for him and the girls. He had eaten most everything they had last night. She moved his arm and slipped out of his embrace, careful not to wake him.

"I thought of you all of the time, Schatzi," he murmured.

She turned around to look at him and smiled.

"You are more beautiful than I remembered."

"Sleep—you are safe now." She leaned over to brush his lips with a kiss. "I need to go out and get something for us to eat before the girls wake up."

"Don't go," he said and reached out for her.

"I will be right back. Don't worry. We will never be apart again," she said and tucked him in. "Sleep."

———————

Word of Stefan's return spread quickly, and the families spent the next couple of weeks talking constantly—catching up with news about the soldiers from Scheindorf and the assimilation of refugees, sharing news about cities after the war and the devastation of Europe, and making plans for what they should do. They had more questions than answers. Uncertainty hung over every conversation.

With the girls in bed, Stefan told the story of the death of Franz Moore, the injury of Stefan Müntz, his own beating by the Czechs, and the disappearance of Stefan Funkenhauser. He shared his concern that his friend had disappeared into a work camp in Siberia. His father knew differently. Once on the train, Stefan Funkenhauser and a few other men had found loose boards in the train car and broken through. They had jumped off the train and run to freedom. Stefan was thrilled to hear such good news!

Stefan also told the stories of the kindness of strangers along the road. He talked about the women who gave him clothes, the man who shared his meager food and apple wine, and Johann Gloss, the flagstone roofer, who provided him with food, shelter, and work. Stefan explained to them that without this man, he might never have made it through the POW camps. His mother, intrigued by the story of Isabelle and the fortune she told, listened intently and nodded.

"I believe what she said," Gertrude said. "You will be successful, and it will be in America."

One night after dinner, Stefan told the best story of all—meeting Captain Thomas Wiehl. His father laughed, slapped his hand on his knee, and smiled for the longest time. He asked Stefan to retell it—with every small detail—repeatedly.

"The Lord intervened. This was not an accident," Gertrude said.

"I agree," said Maria. "He answered our prayers."

"Who would have ever thought that you would run into young Tom? We have to tell Helen someday—when we get to America," his father said.

"Maybe I should write Rosalia?" Gertrude asked.

"Oh, I want to tell the story in person," Judge Revak said. "I can't wait to see the look on her face!"

While Stefan regained his strength, they worked on creating a plan that would give them a new start. The apartment was much too small for two couples and two children. After talking with the authorities, on the day before Christmas, 1945, Stefan, Maria, and the two girls boarded a train along with five other refugee families for a displaced persons camp in Neunkirchen, Austria. The girls cried. They did not want to leave their grandparents. It was Christmas Eve, after all.

When they arrived at the compound for refugees, it was getting dark, snow was falling, and the temperature was dropping fast. The Gieger, Link, Hahn, Weiss, Koch, and Revak families, bundled up in all of their clothes, walked to their assigned building.

"Here it is, number 242," Maria said. She looked at Stefan with questions in her eyes. They had left a cramped but snug apartment. This looked like a huge warehouse. Maria put her arm around Klothilde and hugged her close to keep her warm.

Stefan, carrying Siglinda, opened the door. He looked around and then put his daughter down.

"Stefan," Maria whispered. "I don't believe this."

There was nothing in the building but a pile of trash.

"Mutti, I'm hungry," said Siglinda as she pulled on Maria's coat.

Maria dropped down to her daughter's eye level.

"We're going to play a game and fix up our new place. We need you to help. Okay?"

"Okay, Mutti, but can we eat then?"

Maria smiled. "Yes, we'll find something to eat."

"Will St. Nicholas find us?" Siglinda asked.

Stefan and Maria looked at each other.

"St. Nicholas is very busy tonight," Maria said. "He might not find us. But he will next year."

Siglinda's smile faded.

"I'm sure of it," said Stefan. "He'll find us next year."

Klothilde held her little doll close to her chest and

stood by listening to every word. She was quiet. "Mutti, it's cold in here. My baby needs to go to sleep," she said.

"We'll get her to bed soon," Maria said.

"Let's get organized," Stefan said as he clapped his gloved hands together to keep warm. "We need heat."

"I'll see what I can find for beds," said Albert Hahn. "Magdalena, let's you and I take the boys and see if we can't find some straw for beds." They left the compound to search other buildings.

"Let's find some wood, and we can build a fire. But we need to vent the smoke," said Stefan.

The families scattered and worked until after midnight. They found boards and straw and made beds. They found an oven in an empty barracks and brought that in, then rigged pipes out the windows to vent smoke from the fire. They shared the food they had packed for the journey.

On Christmas morning, they found more wood, made rough tables, and celebrated Christmas. It was not about presents; it was about family and the birth of Jesus Christ. They were happy just to be together, even if they had nothing but each other and their few meager possessions. They all ate from one pot.

Together, the families decided that in order to survive, they needed to be organized. Each of them would have a job. Stefan became the guard. Magdalena Hahn would work with the camp cooks and find enough food for the families. Maria would cook. The girls would help clean up. The boys would search for wood every day.

Stefan, standing outside the building as a guard, talked with everyone who walked by and made friends with the camp cooks, who, when they learned about all of the children in the building, gave him extra bones and potatoes. Maria would make soup and for a few moments, the heat would melt the cold in their bodies. It was a long winter of mending clothes, scavenging for food, and finding wood for fires. But they were together. Life, in its own difficult way, was good.

———•—•———

One day in early spring, while Stefan was standing guard, a woman walked up to him.

"My husband and I are looking for workers," she said.

He was a little suspicious, but she seemed earnest enough.

"What kind of work?"

"We have a restaurant, a bar, and a mill, and we have a horse and four cows. I need a man who can cut grass and take care of the horse. His wife could take care of the cows. "

"Can you wait until two o'clock today?" Stefan asked.

"Yes, but the train leaves at 2:45. Why?"

"Because I can come then—with my family."

"You can cut the grass?"

He laughed. "I was a farmer. Yes, I can cut grass."

"You sure?"

"All my life, I've cut grass."

Stefan shared with her that he, his wife, and their two daughters lived in the compound. They agreed to meet Frau Hofer at the train station before 2:45 p.m. Any place with work would be better than here. That day, Maria packed their possessions, said good-bye to the families in the compound, and left with Stefan and the girls for Losenstein, Austria.

The family traveled on the train through the heavily forested and mountainous region of Upper Austria. It was another journey to the unknown, but it was beautiful. The property manager, Christian Sternberger, met them at the train station. With introductions made, they boarded a wagon pulled by two cows.

"So you can cut grass?" Herr Sternberger asked Stefan.

What is this about cutting grass? Stefan wondered. "Yes, I can cut grass."

"We'll take a look at the grass tonight. You can start tomorrow," Herr Sternberger said. "It will probably take you a week."

Stefan said nothing. He would cut the grass. How could this be such a big deal?

When they got to the farm, the family settled into a tidy two-room cottage behind Anja Hofer's inn. The whitewashed stucco inn was set on a hill of rich green grass. The flower boxes under each black-shuttered window were full of cascading pink and red geraniums. The cottage was a smaller version of the inn. A blue door, flanked by pots of colorful flowers, marked its entrance.

"It's pretty, isn't it, Stefan?" Maria said. "So much nicer for the girls."

He smiled at her. "We'll make it work, just like we always have. Someday, though, we will have a home of our own. I promise."

Maria nodded. "As long as we're together. That's all that matters, Stefan."

While Maria unpacked in the small cottage with the girls, Stefan followed the property manager up the hill. After a short hike, the manager held out his hand and gestured to the panorama before them—a sea of tall grass waving in the wind. Stefan could hardly believe his eyes. The grass was five feet high, and on the steep side of the mountain, it went nearly vertical. It stretched out for acres. Stefan took a deep breath. He would think this through.

The next morning, before dawn, Stefan ate a quick breakfast and headed out with a mowing scythe to cut the grass. He went round and round, rhythmically cutting, carving a path through the grasses, first on the outside, then going back to widen the mowed area. Singing helped pass the time, and he was reminded of his boyhood friend, Franz Moore—fun-loving Franz, now dead. He shook off the sadness of friends lost and years spent as a soldier. He loved being outdoors. The fresh, clean smell of the cut grass cleared his head, and his mind was flooded with happy memories. He wondered about Uncle Anton. Where would he settle? Would he go to America?

In the physical movement of mowing, Stefan found peace and time to think. Work was good. His family was safe, but he wanted more for them. He wanted to be his own boss, with his own house, not working for someone else. He would make this happen, and with God's help, their future would be secure. There were so many unknowns, but he did not want to think about them, not now. He wanted to be a good provider for his family and someday be successful in his own business. The words of Isabelle's fortune kept weaving their way into his mind. Where? Where would he be successful? Here or America?

At about seven that morning, Herr Sternberger found him already mowing.

"Lots to mow here—it will take you all week," he challenged.

"You think so?" Stefan was annoyed, but he did not let it show. "You do your work. I'll do mine, and by tomorrow night, it will be done."

Herr Sternberger shook his head in disbelief and walked away.

———

By 11:00 a.m. on the second day, Stefan was finished cutting the grass. He walked back to the inn where the women were making lunch. The property manager sat at the long dining table drinking apple cider. Herr Sternberger looked up, surprised to see him.

"Okay, this is what we're going to do," Stefan announced. "This afternoon, we need the ladies to spread the grasses to dry. Tomorrow, we'll bind it up and take it home."

"Wait, when are you going to finish it?" Herr Sternberger asked.

"Finish what?" Stefan said.

"When are you going to finish cutting the grass?"

"It's done. I just finished."

"I don't believe it," said Herr Sternberger.

"Go look for yourself," Stefan said.

Herr Sternberger got up and walked out to the fields. Stefan helped himself to a big drink of water while he waited, pleased with himself.

"I don't believe it!" the property manager said when he returned. "I've seen guys work, but I've never seen anyone like you."

After lunch, the women went out to the fields and spread the grass to dry. Stefan went into the woods, cut down saplings, and lashed them together to build a travois for the horse. The next day, as the grasses dried, he loaded the hay on the travois, and the horse dragged it to the barn. He repeated the process until everything was under cover.

At the end of the day, Herr Sternberger, impressed by Stefan's hard work, said, "I would never have believed it if I had not seen it." He slapped Stefan on the back. "Help yourself to the apple wine—anytime, as much as you like. Stefan, you and your family eat what I eat and drink what I drink."

———————

In early April, Stefan, Maria, and the girls planned a visit to Oma and Opa Revak, who had relocated to Steyr, Austria. Frau Hofer, grateful for all of their hard work and budding friendship, offered the use of her wagon for the trip. The girls were excited to see their grandparents for the first time since Christmas Eve. The trip was a new adventure.

As Stefan drove the wagon through the historic village of Steyr, they saw devastation from bombings, but rebuilding had begun. Most of the homes and factories were intact. The stately Lamberg Castle stood timeless and unharmed on a hill above the streets.

Stefan turned down a tree-lined street to find his parent's small house in a well-kept neighborhood, tucked away from the village center. Flowers cascaded from window boxes, and the neighborhood, near the bicycle factory where they worked, was quiet.

Gertrude had been waiting all morning for their arrival. She had been up well before dawn baking. The table groaned with food: her best black rye bread, her son's favorite homemade cherry preserves, sausage, pickles, sauerkraut, cheese, ten-bean soup, and spiced potato cake. She watched for the family through the lacy white curtains of the front windows. She could not wait to see the girls.

Finally, she saw the wagon coming toward the house, and she could see two blonde heads peeking out from behind their parents.

"Opa, come quickly! They're here!"

She did not wait for an answer but raced out the front door as the wagon pulled in front of the house.

Stefan jumped down from the wagon and turned to help Maria off, then the girls one by one.

"Oma," Siglinda said, catching sight of Gertrude, "Do you have candy?"

Gertrude crushed both girls in her arms.

"Siglinda, after lunch. First, say hello to your Oma!" said Maria.

Stefan looked up to see his father approach the family.

"Pop—good to see you," he said. His father's eyes filled with tears, and he wrapped his arms around his son. He turned to hug Maria. "Maria, beautiful as ever."

"Opa! Opa!" Klothilde called and ran into his arms.

"Oh, my heart," said Gertrude, taking out a handkerchief and fanning her face. "We have missed you all, so much."

"Come in, come in," said Opa. "Stefan, let me help you. Your mother has outdone herself once again." He smiled. "Come, girls, there is plenty of food inside. And candy."

Siglinda clapped her hands with joy. Klothilde took her Oma's hand, and they walked inside. Maria and Stefan stood by the wagon, looked at each other, and smiled.

———·•·———

The next day, Maria packed a picnic with bread and cheese, fruit, and a small jug of apple wine. The girls, excited to be with their grandparents and spoiled by their treats, hardly noticed their parents leave.

Maria and Stefan hiked into the foothills of the mountains. The sky was blue, dotted with a few towering white clouds in the west. The colorful wildflowers danced in the wind, and the grasses waved tall. The ground was soft underfoot. Maria took a deep breath. She smelled spring—the earth ready to give birth again, the sweet scent of clover.

She looked at Stefan and smiled.

"We're alone—in this beautiful place!"

"Is this a good place to stop?"

"Yes," she said. "Let's put the blanket down here."

They laid out the old brown blanket on a flat area of grass. They both sat down, and she unpacked the rucksack of food and drink.

Stefan lay with his hands behind his head. The birds called to each other from the trees. The wind softly blew, rustling the leaves as he looked up through the canopy at the endless blue sky.

"This is heaven, I think," he said looking over at

Maria.

"Heaven is where you are," she said.

She leaned over, and he was lost in her hazel eyes, sparkling with happiness, and so full of tenderness. She kissed him, and her lips tasted sweet and soft. He would never have enough of her. He had waited so long.

———•—•———

The summer months were busy with fieldwork. Maria and Stefan worked side by side. Klothilde stayed with Stefan's parents in Steyr for a short period while Siglinda stayed at the inn.

Maria was obsessed with eating apples. Regardless of where she was, she had an apple in her pocket or in her hand. She ate them green, if she had to, all day long. Stefan knew what the craving meant—she was pregnant. He was puzzled. She never had this yearning with the girls. Did this mean the baby was a boy?

In late August, Stefan received an official government envelope, printed in English and German: "United National Relief and Rehabilitation Administration (UNRRA)." The letter ordered the family to relocate to Germany, to a potato farm in the region of Kempten, immediately. He had heard the Austrians wanted those of German heritage sent back in Germany. He had hoped they would be spared this move. It was not to be.

Stefan folded the letter and placed it back into the envelope. When would this end? Maria was pregnant, the girls were happy, and they had work. How would he explain this to them?

His heart ached as he considered another move for

his family. They had been through so much. He and
Maria would have to put on another brave face for the
girls and get on with it.

The day to leave came in October. Stefan stood to
wait for the train with Siglinda held tightly in his arms.
The rail yard was chaotic with activity, trains coming
and going, whistles blowing, refugees and American soldiers milling around. Coal dust fell like flakes of black
snow. Maria held on to Klothilde's hand. Their trunk
was full of all of their belongings, including Maria's precious linens from Scheindorf. They waited their turn,
uncertain of what to expect.

In the throng of people, Stefan was surprised to see
his parents working their way toward them.

"Maria, look!" Stefan nodded and caught Maria's
attention.

"Look, girls," Maria said. "Oma and Opa are here!"

Stefan was relieved they might be together, and the
girls would certainly be happy to be with their grandparents again.

His father was shaking his head as he approached.
"Glad you are here," he said when he reached them.
"This is madness—bureaucratic madness. We had reset-
tled. We had jobs. Now they're moving us again."

"Well, at least we're together," Maria said, smiling.

"They aren't allowing us to go home," Stefan said,
his disappointment showing. "They want those of German
descent out of Austria and back in Germany."

"I'm not sure home is there anymore," Stefan's father

said. "We have to go where they tell us. I can only hope this will be the last time we move."

Stefan looked over and saw Klothilde asking her oma for something—probably a treat. His mother was already digging through her bag.

"Are you going to Kempten too? The potato farm?" Judge Revak asked.

"Yes," Stefan said over the din. A train was pulling into the station.

"Well that's good news," his father shouted. "We'll be together again."

The swarm of refugees headed toward a cattle car. Stefan felt his anger boil at the sight. He had had enough of cattle cars; now his family would have to ride standing while breathing in the stench. He hoped it would not be long. He was worried about Maria. She was strong, but traveling standing up without food, water, or rest would be very hard on her.

He helped everyone into the car. They found a corner near an opening where fresh air provided some relief from the heat and the smell of manure. The whistle blew three long blasts, and the train began to rock with motion.

It was hot. They were crowded together. They quickly drank the flask of water they had packed.

Stefan was relieved when after three hours, the train slowed. The brakes screeched, and the train came to a halt. The door to the car slid open, and people scrambled out—to get food, to get water, to relieve themselves. Everyone needed water, so Stefan took their three-liter jug and jumped off the train. He found a pump, filled the jug, and headed back.

Before he could reach it, the train started to move.

Panicked, Stefan ran. The jug was heavy. He ran as fast as he could, straining to carry the jug. Suddenly he felt something give in his groin. The pain was excruciating, but he kept running—he had to. He could not lose his family! He yelled, and a man reached out and helped him board the train. Stefan dropped the jug of water and leaned over, gulping air. The pain cut through him like a knife. He could hardly move. He could sense that his testicle had swollen. It felt like the size of a large orange. He could hardly stand. He could hardly breathe.

Maria was worried, but in their whispered conversation, they determined that he could not stay with them in this pain. He needed to get off at the next stop, find out what was wrong, and catch up with them later. She would stay with the girls and his parents on the train, and they would go to Ulm. Adding to the complications was their awareness that this was not the direct route to Kempten.

At the next train stop, he got off and found a Blue Cross. He was taken to a hospital for evaluation. Their first diagnosis was a disease caught "from the ladies." Stefan told them he had only been with his wife. They shook their heads in disbelief, and when he balked at their suggestion of bringing Maria in for testing, they pumped him full of shots for nearly four days. He worried about his family.

Meanwhile, Maria and the girls traveled for hours to Ulm and then to Schweinfurt. Temporarily housed in the bunkers built during the war, the girls waited with Stefan's parents while Maria boarded a train and headed back to find Stefan.

By the time she arrived, Stefan was allowed to get out of bed and walk the grounds of the hospital. The swelling was down. He learned he had a hernia. He was still in pain, but he was anxious to get back to his family. He saw Maria before she saw him.

"Maria!" he called.

She looked around.

"Maria!" he shouted again and began to limp toward her. Her tired face lit up with a smile, and he walked as quickly as he could to her.

"Are you all right?" she asked. "We were so worried."

Stefan told her the story—leaving out the part about "being with the ladies" as he knew it would only upset her, especially since it was not true.

"Where is everyone?" he asked.

"They are safe—in Schweinfurt. We are certainly taking the long way to Kempten. Thank goodness the baby isn't due for a while." She gently patted the round of her tummy.

"You must be tired," Stefan said. He put his arm around her and guided her to a shaded bench near a small pond.

"Yes, I'm tired. But someone had to find you! And I thought we'd never be apart again!" She smiled. "But we know how to survive—to make it work. That's for sure! We always help each other, and others help us. And God is always watching." She looked around at the lush trees that encircled the hospital grounds. "Any apples around here?"

He laughed. "I'm sure we can find you some apples!"

Maria and Stefan took the train back to Schweinfurt, met up with the families, and were on the train to the Kempten area via Ulm when Maria passed out. She was exhausted and needed food. The Red Cross intervened and moved her off the train to a hospital. Stefan had to keep going with the girls to Altusried in Kempten. He would get them settled and come back for her.

They reached Altusried around 6 a.m. Stefan, his two daughters, and his parents waited at the train station for the potato farmer to come and pick them up. It was harvest time, and they needed help in the fields. They would provide them shelter in exchange for their work. They waited patiently for hours, but no one came. He worried about Maria.

"Papa, we're hungry," Klothilde said.

"*Brot*, Papa," Siglinda said.

Stefan had no bread—no food of any kind. But how could he not feed his children?

Determined to find them something to eat, he left the girls with his parents and headed into the town. Every bakery he entered required food stamps. He had none, only a little bit of money. Finally, he went into a bakery and explained his situation to the woman at the counter.

"Wait here," she said. She went back into a room. A moment later, she appeared with a large, wrapped loaf of bread. "Here you go," she said. "I have children too; they are always hungry." She smiled.

"Let me give you some money for it," Stefan said. "How much?"

"Nothing—you owe me nothing," she said.

Stefan thanked her for her kindness.

He continued down the street and saw a store with a

huge kielbasa hanging in the window. The sign said, "No stamps needed."

Stefan was overjoyed—he could bring everyone bread and sausage. He tried to buy the entire sausage, but the butcher would not sell it all. He bought as much as he could and walked back to the train station. The food was gone in ten minutes.

While they were waiting, the Leili family arrived and sat down to wait. The Revak girls were happy to be with other children. Playing with them helped pass the time.

Stefan moved to another bench and sat with another man waiting for a ride. The girls came up to him and once again said, "Brot, Papa, we're hungry!"

He sighed, but he could not feed them again right now. He took both of them by the hands and said, "Siglinda, Klothilde, I don't have anything right now. You'll have to wait." A tear slipped down Siglinda's face. She walked away, looking down at her feet.

"What did they want?" said the man sitting next to Stefan.

"They're hungry. They wanted something to eat," Stefan said.

"I'm a baker. Come with me," the man said. Stefan followed the man a short distance. The man went into his shop and came out with two big loaves.

"Keep one for your family," the man said. "And give the other to the other family."

Stefan thanked him and did as he said.

The day stretched on. A wagon came for the Leili family, and they bid them good-bye. It was getting dark. Stefan sat at the train station with the girls and his parents. To pass the time, he and his mother sang folk songs to the girls as they sat and waited. When the sun set, the girls cuddled up with him and slept on the bench. Stefan felt bad. Here he was, a grown man with two children and a third on the way, and he had no place to live—no money, no way to support his family.

Stefan dozed off. He heard a truck rumble down the road toward them. It was about 11 p.m. The truck pulled up at the station, and the bright headlights woke everyone up.

The driver got out of the truck. "I'm looking for the people who are going to the Albrechts. Anyone here?"

"We are going there," said Judge Revak. "My son and his family are also to be placed in the area."

"Oh, they must be with the Heberle family," the driver said. "Get in, all of you. We've got about a fifty-kilometer ride tonight."

The man helped them load their belongings and gave Siglinda and Klothilde a drink of water. Then the wagon lurched forward, and off they went on a bumpy dirt road into the night and their unknown future.

"It's harvest now," the driver said to Stefan. "We work late in the day to harvest the potatoes before they rot. That's why I'm so late."

Stefan nodded. He looked over his shoulder at his daughters sleeping by their oma in the back of the wagon. "The Albrechts will welcome your parents' help on the farm," the man told him.

It was very late when they arrived, but the Albrechts welcomed everyone into their home and cooked food for the refugees.

"Can you tell me where we're staying?" Stefan asked. He was anxious to get the girls settled. "I was told we're to be staying with the Heberles."

"Oh, that's my sister!" Frau Albrecht told him. "They live across the road. You will live with them."

After saying thanks to the Albrecht family for their kind hospitality, Stefan carried Siglinda and a sleepy Klothilde across the road to the Heberle's farm. The house was dark when Stefan approached with his two girls.

Stefan knocked at the door. No response. He knocked again. What would he do if no one answered?

The door opened a slit, and a man peered through.

"I'm sorry to wake you, but we're the Revak family. Your sister-in-law told us this is where we were to stay. We will help you with work in exchange for food and shelter."

The man looked at Stefan suspiciously, and then he noticed the two girls. Siglinda was sound asleep in Stefan's arms and Klothilde was yawning.

"Papa, I'm tired," Klothilde said.

"Come in, come in," Herr Heberle said. Stefan walked in with the girls. Herr Heberle scowled. "I don't know you people," he said. "As far as I know, you could be Communists. We are God-fearing people here. We live by the rules. I only agreed to this because we need help with the harvest. I know nothing about you, but you have two little girls, and they need a bed and some food."

Stefan nodded, determined to make the best of this situation. "Herr Heberle, I was a farmer. We have lost our home and land because of the war. We are of German descent. We are Catholic. I have no money to feed my children, no way to support my family, and my wife who is pregnant with our third child had to be taken to the hospital on the way here. We need your help."

Frau Heberle joined her husband. When she saw the two little girls, she said, "Get them in here, they are tired. Look at that little one, she's sound asleep." She leaned down to Klothilde. "Are you hungry?" Klothilde looked at her father first, as if to ask permission, then at Frau Heberle and nodded.

"I thought so!" Frau Heberle said. "I've got some cheese and bread; that should hold you till breakfast." She smiled and nudged Klothilde to the kitchen.

Herr Heberle still eyed Stefan with mistrust. Stefan followed the frau into the kitchen, feeling the man's eyes bore into his back.

After a quick snack for the girls, Stefan tucked them into bed, and fell into bed exhausted, but his thoughts kept him awake. Would this family work out? How was Maria? When would they find a permanent home again?

The next morning when Stefan woke up, he went into the cooking room and was surprised to find a large bowl of warm farina and a liter of fresh milk on the counter. The smell of the warm cereal drifted into their sleeping room, and Siglinda came out, rubbing her eyes.

"I smell something good, Papa," she said.

"Frau Heberle has left us some breakfast," he said.

"Will she bring it every day?"

"She might if you eat it all and then thank her."

Siglinda sat down at the table.

"I'm hungry. It tastes so good."

Klothilde joined them, and their day began.

A day passed with no word about Maria, then another. Stefan was worried. He worked with Herr Heberle, taking care of the calves, cleaning the barn, and spraying liquid manure onto the fields. One day when they came from the fields for lunch, Maria was there. A nurse had brought her home. She was sitting at the table eating, surrounded by her daughters and Fraus Albrecht and Heberle. The girls chattered nonstop. Maria was quiet, nodding her head and listening.

When she saw him, she looked up and smiled.

Stefan took one look at the dark circles under her eyes and worried even more. She picked at her food, pushing it around her plate. He knelt down beside her and hugged her.

"You are home now. We will take care of you," he said.

CHAPTER TWENTY-THREE

"Not I, nor anyone else can travel that road for you.
You must travel it by yourself.
It is not far. It is within reach.
Perhaps you have been on it since you were born,
and did not know.
Perhaps it is everywhere—on water and land."
Walt Whitman

Altusried, Germany
New Year's Eve, 1946, to 1951

MARIA WAS IN labor. The gray winter day was cold and blustery. A near blizzard blew in as the day length-ened, snow accumulating quickly on the deep crust of ice that covered the frozen ground. Herr Heberle sent Herr Schmidt with the horse-drawn sleigh to pick up Maria and Stefan.

This baby would not be born at home.

As they walked from the house, their boots sank into the new, powdery snow. Stefan helped Maria into the sleigh. Herr Schmidt covered them with a thick green-and-black checkered wool blanket backed with black horsehair.

"Rex was a good horse. Now he'll keep you warm on this ride," Herr Schmidt said to them with a smile as he wrapped the blanket around them. "We'll get you there safely." He winked at Maria.

Maria smiled weakly and clung to Stefan's arm in the back of the sleigh. Though the blanket blocked the wind, they were not sheltered from the blowing snow. The contractions were intense, increasing with the rocking and bumping of the sleigh. The wind whipped her dark hair around her face.

When they got to the hospital, Frau Eicher, the midwife, checked Maria and encouraged her to walk. Maria was worried. She knew this baby was big—bigger than the girls had been. The way she carried the baby—out in front of her—was different. Siglinda's birth had been easy. This labor was already lasting much longer.

The contractions got stronger as she walked with Stefan down the halls of the hospital. They walked into the night. After midnight, she was getting tired, but she did not want to have surgery to have this baby. She would do what the midwife told them to do. They walked until the contractions were so hard she felt her knees go weak. She could feel the pressure of the baby moving lower and deeper inside of her. Finally, she could walk no longer. She had to get into bed.

Maria knew Stefan was talking to her, but she could not hear him. She was in the place where a pregnant woman can only do one thing. She could hardly control the urge to push. The midwife was waiting, the instruments for surgery were waiting, and a doctor was near. She was determined to have this child as she had the others.

"Maria, push! Hold your breath and push!" Frau Eicher said.

As Stefan watched with concern, Maria pushed with all of her might.

"Good, Maria—you're doing well! I can see the crown of the baby's head. Next contraction, push as hard as you can!"

Maria nodded. She took a deep breath as she lay back and rested the short one minute between contractions.

Maria sat up again. Stefan supported her from behind, and Frau Eicher helped her grab her ankles and said, "Push! Push! Push!"

"Aaauggghh!" Maria cried between clenched teeth. She dripped with sweat. This was much harder than Siglinda.

Maria lay back down. The contraction was over.

"One more big push—with the next contraction," Frau Eicher said, "and we'll have this baby."

Maria nodded. The contraction came, and Maria took a deep breath and pushed.

"Take another breath!"

Maria pushed. "Oooooo."

"The baby's coming, the head is out, just going to check around the neck for the cord—wait a minute, Maria. Now, gentle, push."

Stefan breathed a sigh of relief as the slippery red baby slid out of Maria on to the bed. He looked at the baby and said, "It's a boy, Maria! A big boy!"

"He must weigh at least ten pounds," Frau Eicher said, holding him up for Maria to see.

Stefan's eyes filled with tears. They had a son. They named him Rudolf.

As winter turned into spring, Maria recovered slowly from childbirth. Once again, she had hemorrhaged, and she was in terrible pain. The doctor told her that her uterus was tipped and that if she had it removed, the bleeding and pain would stop. But she wanted to avoid surgery, so she took a conservative path of medication, and finally the pain faded.

Stefan lay awake at night wondering how he could support his wife and three children and give them a better life. Klothilde was in school, and Siglinda soon would be. He needed a way to make money. He was grateful to the Heberles and Albrechts, but he wanted more—for himself and his children. So with Herr Heberle's support, he decided to replicate some of the work they had done in Scheindorf, something every community needed and that was perfect for the crops they produced—whiskey.

Stefan needed a still. Herr Heberle suggested that his nephew, Karl, who worked in a factory in Stuttgart, might be able to help. When Karl was home, Stefan met with him and told him what he needed. Karl made a diagram of the still.

"How much will you charge?" Stefan asked.

"Don't worry," said Karl. "We can talk about it later."

About two weeks later, Karl came back and said he had found someone who could help build the still.

"How much?" Stefan asked.

"Don't worry—just give me some whiskey," Karl said.

Herr Heberle agreed to give Stefan a salary and half of the whiskey he produced. Stefan could use the whiskey any way he wanted—to drink, to sell, or to barter.

Stefan's recipe for whiskey began by taking a pail full of rye and soaking it overnight in water. The next day, he spread the rye out on a four-by-eight platform of plywood. Then he waited for it to sprout. When the rootlets were about three inches long, he dried them in the sun. Later, he would grind up the rye malt and add it to the mixture.

He cooked potatoes in fifty-gallon drums and mashed them while they were still hot, then added the rye malt and let them cool. He kept four fifty-gallon drums in the basement of the barn. He added yeast at just the right temperature, usually about 20 degrees Celsius. The drums had to be stored at a steady temperature, and the barn basement was perfect for that. Every morning he stirred the mash, and again at night, and he would taste it—waiting for that sour taste to be just right. He spent a great deal of time in the barn, especially at the end of the process. In fact, the timing was so important to the recipe that the women brought him food because he could not leave. When the mash was ready, it went into the still where it was cooked again and distilled—taking out all of the solids.

Stefan's enterprising spirit found even more opportunities. Each spring and fall, Herr Heberle's sows had litters, sometimes as many as twelve piglets. Stefan asked if he could help raise them. Heberle gave Stefan two piglets of his own in return. Stefan fed them whey, the byproduct that drained when they made cheese. The pigs grew to around two hundred kilograms. In the fall, they butchered the pigs and then smoked the chops and other cuts of pork to preserve the meat. They made sausage, ham, and cured bacon. Stefan kept in mind the words of his father, "We eat everything from the pig except the squeal!"

Stefan found many willing customers for his portion

of the whiskey. One time, he sold nearly the entire batch to Yugoslavian refugees living in barracks in Kempten. With that money, Stefan found a tailor who made suits, dresses, blouses, and coats for his entire family. He traded whiskey for flour, milk, cheese, and other necessities. Maria made wonderful desserts and pastries for the family.

One day his father came to him as he was feeding the pigs. He was scowling.

"Did you give whiskey to your mother?" he asked.

"No, why?"

Judge Revak's face was somber. "She's drunk," he said.

Stefan's heart sank. He had ten one-liter bottles of whiskey in his cooking room. When he went home, he checked. One was missing. He felt terrible. His mother had been sober since leaving Scheindorf. She was a different woman when she was not drinking. He felt responsible for this. They all drank, but they could stop. She could not. He would have to put the whiskey in a safer place where she would not find it.

Next, Stefan approached Herr Heberle about growing tobacco. Cigarettes were one of those luxuries that were hard to afford, but if they grew their own tobacco, they would have cigarettes to smoke, sell, and barter. Heberle agreed, and they grew tobacco, dried it, and cut it fine. Stefan made cigarettes with a little machine.

One summer day, Maria and Stefan were working together in the tobacco field. Klothilde was watching Rudolf. She decided to give her little brother a change of scenery and push his stroller out to the field where they were working. In order to get to the field, she had to open a large gate. She removed the long metal poles and laid them to the side. A farmer with a carriage pulled by four horses drove by, and one of the horses shied and reared up. Klothilde pushed her baby brother out of the way, but she stepped on one of the poles and fell hard. The farmer never stopped.

Klothilde got up. Her shoulder hurt terribly. She used her other arm to push seven-month-old Rudolf to the field to find her parents. Maria was distraught at the sight of Klothilde's arm limply hanging by her side.

Klothilde told them the story.

"You are a very brave girl," her mother said.

"I'll take her into town," Stefan said.

Maria took Rudolf home. Stefan took Klothilde into Altusried, where a doctor was able to manipulate her arm, putting the joint back in place. She had dislocated it, he said. She was quiet throughout all of the pain. Stefan was proud of her.

During the winter, Stefan cut wood in the forest. He met Herr Doerffler, a cabinetmaker, who lived in a house owned by Herr Albrecht. One day, Herr Doerffler stopped by Stefan and Maria's house when Stefan was home having lunch. He offered Herr Doerffler some food and whiskey.

The cabinetmaker took a drink and smiled. "This is good whiskey!"

"We can do business together," Stefan promptly said. "You make us some furniture, and I'll give you whiskey."

"What do you need?"

"I need a bed, a wardrobe, a table, six chairs, and a cabinet for the kitchen."

It was a deal. When the furniture was finished, Stefan found a painter who was willing to work for the old currency, Reichsmarks, and Stefan had newly painted furniture.

Over the years that Stefan worked for the Heberles, his entrepreneurial spirit provided for his family. He raised Angora rabbits and sheared them. Then he made an attachment for Maria's sewing machine so she could spin the fur and knit beautiful sweaters for the girls. After he did work for Herr Drucker, whose son had died in the war, Herr Drucker offered him his son's motorcycle in payment. Stefan could not resist. He took the bike and fixed it up.

But Stefan was still not satisfied. He wanted more for his family.

Aunt Agatha and Uncle Michael had recently relocated and lived not far away. They all went to the same church, so they would see each other on Sundays. All they could talk about was going to America. Stefan felt it was an impossible dream. He was, after all, a former German soldier. Despite what Captain Wiehl had said, he doubted the Americans would ever let him immigrate.

Stefan wanted to be a builder, so he approached Herr Baer, a builder in the area, about a job.

"What kind of work can you do?" Baer asked.

"I'd like to become a mason—to learn bricklaying."

Baer hesitated for a moment. He looked Stefan over and then nodded.

"Come to work on Monday. We'll give this a try."

Work with Herr Baer was a little slow, but Stefan started out patching holes in stucco and learned the business so quickly that he was sent out alone on big jobs—including raising the ceiling on a house by lifting up the whole house and building it back from the bottom up. The work had to be precise so that the roof would fit back on the top of the house.

Every day before he went to work, he took the girls to school on his motorcycle—one on the front and one on the back. Soon they started riding their bikes to school in good weather and skiing to school in the winter. School only went up to the eighth grade, but they went to school five and a half days a week. On the half-day, Saturday, the girls learned how to knit, sew, and cook.

When the weather was cold, there was little work. Stefan spent a lot of time at home. Maria baked wonderful cakes, and Stefan made a little paper cone and piped frosting through it to decorate them. Their life with the three children was busy and good. Stefan's time in the army and the POW camps faded away like a bad dream, though sometimes his memories came back to haunt him in bad dreams or night sweats. He would wake up moaning. Maria was always there to comfort him. His missing trigger finger throbbed in the cold weather. He missed playing the accordion. Could he play again? He wanted to try; he so loved music.

One Sunday after Mass, Uncle Michael pulled him aside.

"We've got our papers for America," he said. Stefan's heart fell, thinking about how he was now losing another family member. Yet he was happy for them.

"We want you to come too," Michael said.

"I don't know if that is possible," Stefan said.

"Your father and mother want to go. We want you to be with all of us. You can make a better life there—for your family. You are a hard worker. You will be successful. Your dreams can come to life, Stefan."

"I will talk it over with Maria. The government will

have to clear me to go."

"We will help, you know, anything you need. We will help."

Stefan sighed. He felt a terrible sense of loss. His family, fractured by war, in peace would soon be separated by an ocean. Despite his uncle's assurances, it was an ocean he had little hope of ever crossing.

———•—•———

Uncle Michael and Aunt Agatha made a life for themselves in America. Uncle Michael found a job right away as a superintendent in an apartment building. He was handy, could fix just about anything, and was not afraid of hard work. The letters from his aunt and uncle were full of the differences in America. In one letter, they talked about having a refrigerator. Maria and Stefan had no clue what they were talking about.

His aunt implored Stefan to send their birth certificates, as she and Michael would try to sponsor them. Stefan did as she asked, though he was not optimistic. The months went by, and finally, he received a letter from the International Refugee Organization in Munich. He went to Munich to meet with the American authorities who could clear him to immigrate. When they asked him if he had been in the German army, Stefan said yes, and the interview ended.

His aunt and uncle did not give up. Another year went by, and another letter came from Munich. He went again. They asked if he had been in the military. Again, he said yes; again, the interview ended. He had been right. There was no way he could go to America.

Stefan's father came to see him one day.

"We got our papers—to go to America," he said.

Stefan nodded, but the words had hit him like a blow. Once again he was torn. His mother and father had nothing here now but a place to live. His father traded for some work, but they lived day to day, merely existing. Their life was nothing like it had been in Scheindorf, where they were landowners and farmers, his father the mayor, a respected and influential man in the region. He knew it was best for them to go. But how could he stand to lose them?

"Pop, you need to go. All of your life, you have wanted to go back to America. Mama too. You will make a better life there. Your life is nothing like you had before. Go; make a better life for yourself."

———

A few days later, Stefan's father went to Munich. The papers were ready, and the date for their departure was set. Judge Revak hesitated.

"I can't go," he said to the American officer. "I have just one son—he was in the German army. He had to serve. He had no choice. They will not let him come to America. I just can't go and leave him."

The officer leaned forward in his chair.

"Herr Revak, I can't tell you what to do, but let me tell you something. I would suggest that you go to America. At this moment, at the United Nations in New York, the protocols for immigration are under revision. In six months, I'm quite sure they will open everything up, and anyone will be able to go, even men who served in the military."

———•+•———

Judge Revak returned from Munich and told Stefan the story.

"Pop, you have to go," Stefan said. "It will be better for you and Mama. We'll be fine."

Stefan heard the words he spoke, but in his heart, they were not the truth. His life was fine—he was happy, but he wanted more. He wanted the richness of life they had had before the war when he owned a business, worked his family's land, and had a home. But his father—no, his father could not seriously consider staying here. As much as he hated to lose them, it was best for his parents to go.

Another thought crept into his mind.

"Pop, have you ever thought about why Mama started to drink again? She is unhappy. You lost everything when you left Scheindorf. You lost your land, your home, your position in the community. She used to talk about hopes and dreams. She was always hopeful we would go to America. You have to go there—for her."

Stefan's father looked down and nodded.

Stefan's parents went to America in 1951.

They wrote frequently. Stefan's father found work in New York City, also as a super, in an apartment building. An apartment came with the job, as well as a salary. Living in New York was an adventure; there was always something to do.

In one letter, Gertrude wrote about television: "We can see people singing and dancing. We can hear music and the news." They raved about it.

Stefan and Maria looked at each other.

What in the heck was television?

CHAPTER TWENTY-FOUR

"Do not think of today's failures,
but of the success that may come tomorrow.
You have set yourselves a difficult task,
but you will succeed if you persevere;
and you will find a joy in overcoming obstacles.
Remember, no effort that we make
to attain something beautiful is ever lost."
Helen Keller

Germany
1952

STEFAN FOUGHT AGAINST the freezing winds of February as he pulled the sled loaded with firewood to the cottage door. He unloaded the sled and started to stack the half-cord of wood against the wall so it would be easy to reach. It got dark so early this time of year, and it was snowing again! The rhythmic knock of wood against wood was a good sound—it meant warm fires and fresh-baked bread.

Maria opened the cottage door and looked out.

"I thought I heard you out here," she said, smiling. "Come in out of the cold. I have some hot soup and a surprise for you."

"Just a few more logs," he said. "I can already taste your soup!"

Finishing up, Stefan opened the door to the cottage, closed it quickly against the cold, and hung his coat up to dry on a hook. He walked into the small kitchen, where the wood stove was hot and Maria was stirring the most fragrant soup—deep, rich brown broth with chunks of pork and loads of vegetables. Candles were burning on the table. The girls were playing with their dolls, and Rudolf was making high-pitched noises as he attempted to play his father's harmonica. Stefan had acquired the harmonica in a trade. It was not an accordion, but it was music, and he loved to play.

Stefan sat down at the table and saw a letter. He picked it up. It was postmarked Munich, February 1, 1952, and was stamped *Dringend*. What could be so urgent?

Stefan looked up at Maria. She shrugged her shoulders.

"Maybe it's good news," she said.

Stefan opened the envelope and pulled out the letter. He scanned it quickly—then again. Then he put it down on the table, wordless.

"Read it! Read it out loud!" Maria said.

Stefan could hardly speak. He swallowed and read, "You are to report to Munich on Tuesday, February 7, to complete your family's application to immigrate to the United States of America."

He jumped up and walked over to his smiling wife.

"We've been approved! We're going to America!"

He wrapped his arms around her, lifted her up until her feet were off the ground, and twirled her around.

"Stefan stop! You'll hurt yourself!" she laughed.

When he put her down and pulled away, he looked into her tear-filled eyes and saw a trembling smile on her lips.

"I wanted this so much for us," he said. "I did not know how much until this very moment. It is the right thing to do. I know it is the right thing to do."

She nodded, and tears of joy slid down her cheeks.

They had to quickly sell or give away almost everything—the precious furniture they had built, the motorcycle he loved, the bikes and skis, the cooking pans, the children's toys, all but some clothes. The only thing they had left from their life in Scheindorf was Maria's precious linens. Everything they carried had to fit in their travel trunk.

Siglinda hugged her doll to her chest. "Mutti, she's just a little doll. I'll carry Heidi."

Maria smiled gently. "I know you feel bad about saying good-bye to Heidi—especially since Oma made her such beautiful clothes and Frau Heberle knitted her such a pretty sweater. I promise that when we get to America, Oma will make you new clothes for a new American doll. Let us leave Heidi here. Let one of your friends adopt her and keep her in Germany."

Siglinda looked down, holding the doll tightly.

"Are you sure?"

"Yes," Maria said, nodding. "You will have a new American doll."

Maria felt a tug of sadness in her heart. It was difficult

to take away everything familiar to her children—their friends, their clothes, their few possessions, their home—but it was necessary. Life was not about possessions. A rich life was about love of family, faith in God, good health, and perseverance through hard times. They would make new friends. They would find many ways to live successfully. They would build a new life in America. They had started over before. They would do it again.

———————

The Revak family returned to Munich in early March, 1952. From there, they would take a train to Bremen, where they would await departure to America. As they walked toward the train station, Herr Baer's comments to Stefan about leaving Germany stuck in his mind. He was sorry to see Stefan leave. He urged him to stay. But it was not to be. Stefan's feet were set on the path to America. They had been for a long time.

Walking down the streets, Stefan saw that the continuing tragic effects of war on the city that had been the Nazi stronghold. Though he tried to put it behind him, the taint of war was always around the next corner, waiting to remind him of the pain of the past. Munich had lost nearly half of its population during the war. The city was under massive reconstruction. It would take years for the bricks and mortar to restore a semblance of Munich's former self. It would take even longer for the German people to recover. Stefan had to move on.

Even though his family had a long journey ahead of them—a journey to the unknown—Stefan's heart felt lighter than it ever had been. He felt more like a boy

than he had as a child. He had a new and different life
ahead of him now. His excitement had been building
since he received the letter, and his mind buzzed now
with thoughts and ideas of what he might do in America.
He knew he would look for work immediately. He wanted
to run a business and hoped that his experience would
prepare him for something America needed.

Though it was winter, the day was sunny and bright.
The family leisurely walked down the sidewalk to the
train station, looking in the shop windows, laughing and
talking. The girls looked in the toy store window, pointing
and smiling. Klothilde held on to Siglinda's hand while
Maria strolled behind them with Rudolf.

Then Maria looked around. Stefan was not with
them anymore.

She gathered up the three children and retraced
their steps. They found Stefan in a music store. He was
looking at an accordion—a beautiful Hohner accordion.
He fingered the mother-of-pearl inlay and ran his hand
across the rich grain of the wood, lost in time. He did
not notice Maria and the children standing by him for a
few minutes.

She stood close to him—waking him from his reverie.

"It's beautiful, isn't it?" he said.

"Yes, it is beautiful," she said.

"But we can't afford it," he said.

"You miss playing, don't you?" she said.

He nodded and sighed.

She pulled a small purse out of her pocket. "I've
been saving this for many years—little by little—to
finally buy you another accordion. Obviously, this one is
calling to you."

"Oh, I can't," he said, surprised and touched by his

wife's gift.

"Stefan—you've given up a great deal. You have suffered much. If this would give you pleasure, we must buy it. I love to hear you sing, and it will bring back happy memories of days before war, of festivals and dances, of times before we starved, before we were apart. Music in our life and in our home will bring you peace and joy. You cannot walk away from this. This is a sign of hope that has been put on our path."

Stefan thought for a moment. He continued to touch the keyboard. Perhaps she was right, his Maria—perhaps this was a sign of the future.

He smiled with a new thought. "Do you think Rudolf will learn to play?"

"I don't know. Rudolf must find his own way. This is something you should buy for you—for now," she said, smiling.

When they arrived in the Bremen train station, the Revak family was loaded on to US Army buses. Taken to Camp Grohn, a massive military and displaced persons camp, they would spend six weeks in quarantine before they could depart for America. At the camp, the family was shown to their quarters, informed of mealtimes and directions, and told where they could and could not walk.

Stefan had had enough of camps, but in this one, he knew they would stay only six weeks, there was plenty of food and cigarettes, and his family was together. It was a small sacrifice to make.

During the six weeks, each member of the family received a physical examination and all of the necessary injections for travel. The children found other children their age, and they were able to play together. Rudolf was now five, Siglinda was ten, and Klothilde was nearly fourteen. Stefan was amazed at the number of displaced persons in the camp. He asked one of the physicians and learned that as many as five thousand refugees were housed here at a time.

The camp held a series of lectures the families were required to attend. Instructors, speaking German, provided an orientation to life in the United States of America. The refugees heard an overview of American history, learned the steps to becoming a citizen, and were given information about currency and measurements, tips on finding employment, and an introduction to social customs. They also were taught some basic English phrases: "How much does this cost?"; "Please" and "thank you"; "Where is this street?"

One night when they were in bed, Maria whispered to Stefan, "I'm never going to be able to learn this language. My mouth does not know how to form the sounds. I feel so stupid."

"We'll get it," he said. "In fact, I think the children will help us as much as anyone. We need to encourage them to speak English. We can speak German with our friends and relatives, but we need to make American friends—and so do the children. We must be the example."

She rolled her eyes. "I don't know," she said. "This is really hard."

"Go to sleep, Schatzi. Tomorrow is day fourteen of our time here. Can you believe it?"

During the remainder of their days, they walked through the camp, met other refugees, and heard their stories, played with other children, and stopped at the base sweet shop. The children loved ice cream, and so did Stefan. It became a routine to go for a walk after dinner and stop in for a scoop or a piece of candy. Stefan's small reserve of money was dwindling quickly.

Though it was awkward at first to play the accordion without his index finger, Stefan adapted and practiced to get better. At night, he would play the accordion for anyone who cared to listen. People would come from all over the camp, drawn by the music. The children would dance and clap their hands, and the parents would listen to the traditional folk songs and reminisce about happier times before war. Though it was a time of reflection and waiting, it was also a great time of hope.

———•·•———

Finally, quarantine over, they boarded a large military ship. They learned it would carry between eight and nine hundred refugees, plus crew. The family were given separate quarters. Rudolf and Stefan berthed with the men near the center of the ship, while Maria and the girls were with the women, below deck at one end of the ship.

The crew and refugees who were able worked on board. Stefan painted the tall ship's smokestacks. He was not fond of the job. It was dangerous and cold. Sometimes he felt he was the only one working, there were so many people seasick. Maria and the girls, hit hard by the constant movement of the ship, were incapacitated by nausea and vomiting. Klothilde had a particularly difficult time. After a few days, Stefan was able to move them midship to give them some respite from the rocking and rolling of the boat.

Almost no one showed up for meals except for Stefan and Rudolf. One day, out of all of the refugees, they were the only two who came to breakfast.

"Nothing bothers you two, does it?" said one of the cooks as he piled their plates full of eggs, bacon, and grits. "Looks like you're on a private cruise—no one else comes to eat."

Rudolf was worried about his mother and sisters. They had not eaten for days. So while no one was looking, he pocketed four hard-boiled eggs. He stole down to where they were staying and knocked on the door. Maria answered, hugged him, and brought him into their small room. The girls were too sick to come up for fresh air on the deck. Klothilde looked gray. Siglinda was asleep.

Maria smiled. "How's my boy?"

"Mutti, I brought you some food."

"Oh," Maria said.

He handed her the eggs.

It took everything in her power not to vomit from the smell, but she took the eggs and managed a smile.

"Thank you. You are a good boy. Now go back to your father. We need to rest. I'll see you soon."

Rudolf looked around the small space, frowned, and went back to Stefan. He hoped his mother would eat the eggs and get stronger quickly.

When he was gone, Maria got up, walked out of their quarters, and immediately threw the eggs in the trash, gagging all the way.

New York City, New York
The United States of America
April 27, 1952

Finally, after eleven days at sea, the ship navigated into New York Harbor. Everyone was on deck, crowding and leaning over the rails, cheering and waving. The Revak family shivered in the spring air, but they had to see New York—a sight they had dreamed of for many years. Tugboats surrounded the ship, blowing their deep horns, guiding the ship into port.

"The Statue of Liberty—to the left," blared through the ship's public address system.

Every head turned to see the incredible sight of the huge green woman welcoming them—*them*—to America.

Stefan's heart was pounding with excitement. He could not believe it was finally happening. He stared at the Statue of Liberty, and tears filled his eyes. He looked over at Maria and saw tears falling down her cheeks as she too stared at the monument.

Rudolf tugged at Stefan's coat to get his attention.

"Who is she, Papa?" Rudolf yelled over the wind and noisy crowd of refugees.

The cacophony of sound was loud, so Stefan crouched down, wrapped his arms about Rudolf, and spoke into his son's ear.

"The Statue of Liberty—or Lady Liberty—is a symbol of freedom to all of us who come from other countries."

"Why?"

"The people who come here are looking for shelter and a better life, coming to a land where they will not be punished for their religion or beliefs."

"Were we punished, Papa?"

"No, not for our religion—but others were."

"Then why are we here?"

Stefan smiled and wrapped Rudolf's scarf closely around his neck. Then he picked him up so Rudolf could see over the railing. He held him close. Maybe Rudolf would remember a little bit of this day and what his father had said to him in New York Harbor.

"We are here to make a better life for us—to make a home—to own property again—to build and run our own business. It will not happen overnight. It will take time. You can do anything here, if you do it one-step at a time. If you work hard, you can do anything. We are here to contribute our talent and skill to America. We are here to be with family—your oma and opa—our aunts and uncles and cousins. People who work hard in this country can achieve anything they put their minds to—everything they want for their family."

Rudolf listened closely.

"I want the best for you—for your sisters and your mother. America is called the Land of Opportunity. We will do it step by step. You can do anything, Rudolf, if you work hard. That is why we are here."

WRITER'S NOTE

"Life is a journey, not a destination."
Ralph Waldo Emerson

IT IS TIME to separate fact from fiction. Let us begin with what we know is true. This book was born from some thirty hours of audiotapes and transcripts of Stefan Revak (1914–1994) and his wife, Maria (1921–2013), as they shared their stories, along with the memories of their three children: Hilda (Klothilde) Revak Gloss, Linda (Siglinda) Revak Muller, and Rudy (Rudolf) Revak. The names, dates, and historical events in the Table of Historical Events and Characters in the front of this book are accurate, to our knowledge.

The land where this story begins lies at the western edge of the mountains of Transylvania, Hungary. The Satu Mare area, often ravaged by Turks, had been a part of many countries. In 1708, the new landowner, Hungarian Alexander Karolyi, planned to clear the primarily forested land, create settlements, and develop farmland and pastures. The area needed farmers, loggers, and artisans. The immigrants who built the village of Scheindorf and other settlements came from many countries, but predominantly from those areas known as Germany, Romania, Slovakia, Austria, and Hungary.

The Holzli and Revak families were two of the early German families to settle in the area. Sometime in the mid to late 1800s, Vincent Revak married Magdalena Holzli. They were farmers and knew very little of life outside of their region in Austria-Hungary. Their family grew to include Theresia, Johan, Josef, Michael, Anton, Agatha, and Stefan, who was born on September 18, 1889. Not too far away, John Erli married Julianna Teichmann. John and Julianna had eight children: Josef, Rosalia, Johan, Michael, Andrew, Stefan, Theresia, and Gertrude, who was born on September 11, 1893.

The courtship of Stefan Revak and Gertrude Erli was not the typical romance of the time. In 1910, Gertrude, at the age of sixteen, traveled alone to the United States. She worked in New York City as a governess-housekeeper. She was quite a beauty, and Stefan Revak was a young man who knew what he wanted. The letters flew back and forth while she was away, and in 1914, right after the New Year, she returned home to be married in February.

Life was not easy, and they were poor, but they were bright and ambitious. On December 18, 1914, their son was born. They named him Stefan. He would be their only child. When their son Stefan was born, the village of Scheindorf was located in Hungary, or perhaps it would be more precise to say it was located in Austria-Hungary-Romania. The village was a melting pot of cultures and religions.

Josef Ditzig was born on February 19, 1896, one of five children born to Josef and Helena Ditzig. His wife, Maria, born on June 25, 1900, was one of four children born to John Leili and Magdalena (Manz) Leili. Josef and Maria Ditzig did not live far from the Revak family.

They had two daughters, Maria and Mathilda. Their first daughter, Maria, was born on January 4, 1921, and Mathilda in 1926.

When Stefan Revak married Maria Ditzig in 1937, Scheindorf was a tight-knit community of around one thousand people. The families were mostly farmers or tradespeople who were skilled blacksmiths, weavers, tailors, carpenters, and masons. There were stores in town, though most of the villagers grew their own food, harvested their own grapes for wine, made their own whiskey, and raised cattle, pigs, chickens, and sheep for meat and bees for honey. The people of Scheindorf spun flax into thread, wove thread into cloth, and made their own clothes. Villagers bartered for goods, trading whiskey for cloth or grinding wheat for flour. The town had a school and a Catholic church. While their homes and shops were in the village, the land they farmed and managed fanned out for kilometers in all directions.

The chronicle of Stefan's time as a Romanian soldier, as a conscripted German soldier in World War II, and in his postwar progression through POW camps in Jägersgrün, Nuremberg, and Anspach, along with most of the people and events that he encountered, are true. Records of actual conversations and names of people involved do not exist. Battle details and most locations were sketchy in the transcripts. Therefore, the writer created conversations and people who were credible to the period and the story. The details of World War II extracted from history and mentioned in the book are from the References that follow.

Stefan faced many dangers and challenges during and after the WWII. Yet the tapes reveal guidance and protection in his life. His determination and strong will, described in the situations found in the tapes, reveal a man who suffered greatly yet persevered through beatings, starvation, and lack of shelter. The Revak family believes that Maria's constant prayers protected him, and Stefan's self-reliance and strength of will to survive and find his family dictated his every action. His love for Maria was a homing beacon that guided him through many dark days.

Many believe that there is no such thing as coincidence. Stefan's fortuitous meeting with the American "judge," the very same young boy his father had befriended in America in 1920–24, actually happened. This indeed changed the course of his life.

The Revak family's journey as World War II refugees from their home in Scheindorf to Altmünster, Austria, to the displaced persons camp in Neunkirchen, then to Losenstein, Austria, and on to Altusried, Germany are all true. Their journey as refugees lasted from 1944 to 1952. Many of the names of the people they met have been lost in time, but the kindness of the strangers who shared food, shelter, or clothing and gave them the opportunity to work will always be remembered. These examples and situations are clearly described in the Revak tapes and transcripts.

The family's dream to live in the United States of America began in 1910 when Gertrude first traveled there to work. The journey to realize that dream took over forty years. During those forty years, the family in Europe suffered through two World Wars, three POW camps, and eight years as refugees before coming to the United States in 1951 and 1952.

It is appropriate to conclude this journey with a quote from the man who inspired the title of this book,

Ralph Waldo Emerson:

"The purpose of life is not to be happy.
It is to be useful, to be honorable, to be compassionate,
to have had it make some difference
that you have lived
and lived well."

REFERENCES

Axworthy, Mark. *The Romanian Army of World War II*. Oxford: Osprey Publishing Limited, 1992.

Beevor, Anthony. *Stalingrad: The Fateful Siege: 1942–1943*. New York: Penguin Books, 1999.

Emerson, Ralph Waldo. *Emerson: Essays and Lectures*. Edited by Joel Porte. New York: Literary Classics of the United States, 1983.

Feigel, Lara. *The Bitter Taste of Victory: Life, Love, and Art in the Ruins of the Reich*. New York: Bloomsbury Press, 2016.

Gray, Julian. "Bombing of Vienna," *Interrogating Ellie*. Accessed October 11, 2016. http://www.interrogating-ellie.com/bombing-vienna/.

Hargreaves, Richard. *Hitler's Final Fortress, Breslau 1945*. Barnsley, South Yorkshire: Pen & Sword Books, Ltd, 2011.

Hilton, Ella E. Schneider. *Displaced Person: A Girl's Life in Russia, Germany, and America*. Louisiana State University Press, 2004

Miller, Donald L. *The Story of World War II*. New York: Simon and Schuster, 2001.

"Nuremberg Trials." *History*. Accessed September 21, 2016. http://www.history.com/topics/world-war-ii/nuremberg-trials.

Schimpf, Adolf, and Adolf Schimpf. "Not Enough Names in Scheindorf: A Story from New Jersey in the USA," Accessed July 19, 2016. http://www.scheindorf.de/csm/scheindorf-namesstory.htm.

Schmied, Stefan. "Evacuation of the Swabians," Accessed October 11, 2016. http://www.dvhh.org/heritage/Boyle/-Schmied/evacuation-of-the-swabians-15-Schmied~Boyle.

Schmied, Stefan. "History of a Satu Mare Swabian Village," translated from German in 1997 by Anne Julie Weiss Boyle. Self-published by Stefan Schmied, 1970.

Shepherd, Ben H. *Hitler's Soldiers: The German Army in the Third Reich*. New Haven: Yale University Press, 2016.

Shirer, William L. *The Rise and Fall of the Third Reich: A History of Nazi Germany*. New York: Simon & Shuster, 2011.

"Swabians in Scheindorf." *Sathmar*. Accessed October 11, 2016. http://www.dvhh.org/sathmar/history/3-swabians.htm.

Thomas, Nigel. *The German Army in World War II*. Oxford: Osprey Publishing Limited, 2002.

Thomas, Nigel and László Pál Szábó. *The Royal Hungarian Army in World War II*. Oxford: Osprey Publishing Limited, 2008.

Weyr, Thomas. *The Setting of the Pearl: Vienna under Hitler*. New York: Oxford University Press, 2005.